VITAL PRACT

Stories fr
the Healing Arts:
The Homeopathic and
Supervisory Way

by SHEILA RYAN

Sea Change
Portland, UK

Published in the UK by Sea Change

2 Bow and Arrow Cottages
223 Church Ope Road, Portland, Dorset DT5 1JA U.K.
Website: www.seachangeuk.com
Email: info@seachange.co.uk

British Library Cataloguing in Publishing Data

A catalogue record for this book is available from the British Library

ISBN 0-9547867-0-X

This book contains general information only. The author accepts no liability for injury, loss to anyone acting on the contents of this book. No responsibility is accepted for any errors or omissions in the contents of this book.

Grateful acknowledgement is made to the following authors and publishers for permission to reprint extracts from previously published material:

"The Journey" by Mary Oliver in *Staying Alive*. Ed Neil Astley. Bloodaxe Books.

Women Who Run With The Wolves by Clarissa Pinkola Estes. Random House.

Looking For Spinoza by Antonio Damasio published by William Heinemann. Used by permission of The Random House Group Limited.

"Gender Issues in Supervision" by Marina Jenkyns in *Dramatherapy Theory and Practice 3* Ed. Sue Jennings; by kind permission of Routledge.

Suicide and the Soul by James Hillman used by permission of Spring Publications Inc.

Supervision in the Helping Professions by Peter Hawkins and Robin Shohet, OUP.

Signatures Miasms Aids by Misha Norland, Yondercott Press and

The Substance of Homeopathy and *An Insight into Plants* by Rajan Sankaran, HMP.

Printed by Antony Rowe, Ltd. Chippenham, U.K.

Cover design and illustrations by Nick Ford

Text design, layout and typesetting by Betsy Levine

DEDICATION

Vital Practice is dedicated to the Maun Homeopathy Project in Botswana. The project has begun to provide free homeopathic treatment to people affected by HIV and AIDS. It aims to sponsor the training of Botswanan homeopaths, for which your support and donations are welcome.

Enquiries see www.homeopathybotswana.com.

ACKNOWLEDGEMENTS

Heart felt thanks to

Robin Shohet — always minimum intervention delivered in potency.

Brita Andrews for the alchemy of our Dorset walks.

Jim Kimmis for his poet's mind and writing a proper letter.

Julia Hunn who rocks.

Betsy Levine for that hesitation before she tells you what's on her mind — always worth the wait.

Nick Ford for his wizardry — how do his designs do that?

Kathy Lukas and Jo Daly guardian angels of the work at the School of Homeopathy, New York

All the patients, clients, students, practitioners and supervisors whose stories over the years have contributed to the making of this book.

Particular thanks to Sea Change workshop participants from whose willingness, creativity and compassion many of the ideas in this book have emerged.

All who will recognise themselves here and who are not acknowledged by name, since their stories generously shared, have become a part of all of us.

Misha Norland Poet and Principal of The School of Homeopathy, Devon. My homeopathic mentor.

My husband Douglas Stem for being alongside

and son Tom whose suggestion it was to fly with the Kite.

TABLE OF CONTENTS

PREFACE

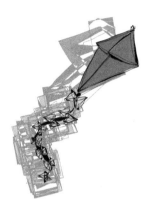

This book is called *Vital Practice:* 'Vital' in paying attention to what is important in any interaction — the motivation. What is it moves me to write this book or you to read it? 'Practice' reminding us to drop the fantasy of perfection in favour of being 'good enough.' (Bettleheim, 1976)

Every tale has gifted me with new insight. Since writing takes on a life of its own, even purposeful prose takes off in surprising directions sometimes. The subversive aims will no doubt become clearer as we go. The stories I intend to tell are these:

1. How simply being 'present' to the moment, actively listening to what is here, contributes to healing. The stories tell something of the qualities of healing relationship.

2. How practicing homeopathy in a supervisory way helps us be more present. The stories tell of supervision as what I am calling a 'quality of looking'.

3. How a homeopathic approach to supervision in turn contributes to rapid, gentle and lasting change. (Hahnemann, 1842, Aphorism 2) The stories tell of homeopathy as guide to healing relationship in general and to supervisory relationship in particular as well as being a principled approach to prescribing potentised remedies.

These threads pull through the stories though not always in a straight line; the tale comes out a little bit here and a little bit there, repeated like this or put like that; in the way we perhaps talk about what ails us. Sometimes tales weave together to make new ones. At other times they stick faithfully to one voice. In every case, where original language is used, the people on whom the story is based have seen the chapters in which they appear. The question *"Whose story is it anyway?"* is at the ethical heart of the project.

Each chapter includes commentary along with suggestions for your own story-making and homeopathic supervision. These can be practiced by yourself, with another or in a group. I hope that you will be encouraged to write your own stories; to see what it is you do to contribute to healing relationship and to celebrate this everyday miracle wherever it occurs.

Each story cross references to others so that the book can be started anywhere and make some sense — or nonsense to you.

Practicing a healing art is simple; not easy or superficial, but simple. Talking about it isn't. I use ordinary words in specific ways and make up new phrases in an attempt to describe what happens. These concepts may strike you as jargon. I hope not. I use them because they give meaning to what is observed. They interrupt conventional ways of seeing. If they get in your way, please chuck them out. Let the stories speak to you.

Words with specific meaning are indicated by *italics* in the text and defined in the glossary at the end of the book.

References are sprinkled throughout. These are listed at the back and are intended to help locate ideas in historical and social context as well as to assist you with further inquiry into your practice and supervision.

What this isn't is a comprehensive text book on the art and craft of supervision. There are very good generic texts out there and these are referred to. If you are new to supervision, then it is recommended you read from these more systematic and inclusive guides.

In the 'Vital Kit,' also at the end of the book, are guides to practicing a *dynamic supervision* in a variety of contexts. These include self supervising, live clinical group supervision including 'bare foot' situations and supervision by phone and email. 'Vital Kit' also contains basic guides to making and maintaining working relationship, contracting and detailed notes on preparing for the art of healing relationship in therapeutic and supervisory settings, in a *triad*.

Vital Practice is an attempt to capture in story, practice and conversation something of the nature of the homeopathic and supervisory way in the hope that you will be inspired, like the kite flyer in Chapter Two, to 'have a go'…

INTRODUCTION

The Homeopathic and Supervisory Way

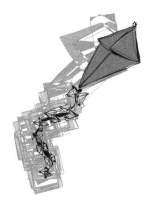

*V*ital Practice is a collection of stories from supervision of the healing arts. The tales could just as easily come from teaching, social work and other professional helping relationships. They could come from marriage, friendship and family life, since healing and diseasing belong to relationship — with ourselves, each other and the environment.

The focus of this collection is on the supervisory matrix because its purpose is to make compassionate inquiry into what is happening. Supervision is considered here to be a 'quality of looking' which attempts to be present to 'what is.'

In telling the stories we meet along the way with eternal questions:

Are some people healers and others not?

Do we think we can heal anyone but ourselves?

What is the difference between healing and curing diseases?

The stories explore specifically a homeopathic approach to supervision and by turn a supervisory approach to homeopathy. The invitation however is to all practitioners of the healing arts and all who would make healing relationship, to make connection with our common task; to adapt, survive and flourish in a continually changing environment.

Feeling for the Way

The homeopathic and supervisory way is simple in essence. It is to attend to healing in accepting what is present 'here and now.' After all, aren't we doing what we can already to adapt, survive and flourish? It's hard enough accepting what we are doing without trying to force a change to doing something completely different! The difficult thing is to see what is happening in the first place and then, even harder, to accept its presence without condition.

This habit of noticing and accepting 'what is,' when applied to clinical practice, is supervision.

In a spiritual context it is the path of enlightenment.

In the context of relationship it is the way of healing.

Relationship

Beginning then with relationship to ourselves:

Morning Pages:

How did you feel when you woke this morning? How did you greet the day? First thoughts? First awareness of body and mind? First conversation with yourself, with your god, with another? Dreams remembered?

To begin the day with morning pages; filling two or three sheets of a daily journal with dreams, mind clutter, feelings, anxieties, woes and hopes, can leave us in a clearer, cleaner, more responsive state for the day that lies ahead. It can prepare us for noticing 'what is'. We begin to notice what we are attached to, what obstacles there are

> between us and accepting ourselves. This is as private as a morning shit and can be just as satisfying. Just let it go; don't hold on, edit, judge or hesitate; let the hand do the writing. (Cameron, 1994)

At the heart of relationship is intention. Is motivation. Is movement. Any relationship can contribute to healing or to dis-easing. What do we intend when we relate to each other?

Focus on a relationship. It may be to your practice of a healing art. It may be to a particular client, supervisee or supervisor.

What is your intention in being in this relationship? What motivates you?

What do you love?

What are you really interested in?

What do you want to know?

What have you found out?

Take a moment to write down whatever comes to mind without judging or censoring it.

What is your relationship like?

If it were an animal, what animal would it be?

If a plant, what plant?

If an element, what element?

If a voice, what would it sound like or say?

What music would it play?

In considering our relationships in metaphor like this, we can sometimes get a sense of them in ways we can't get to by literal description. It can bring surprising insight. Have a go.

And what about our relationship to values, beliefs and ethics? The true meaning of profession is to profess; to declare aloud. What is it I declare aloud? What do I profess? What have I faith in? What do I know with such certainty that I profess it, proclaim it aloud?

What do I believe with a passion?

What is true and what isn't?

Write it down, without aforethought. If you know what you believe, really know it, you can write it down.

Write it down as your manifesto proclaiming to the world.

Write it down as a song to be sung, news to be called out by a town cryer, a sermon, a poem, a prayer.

Or begin by writing it down as morning pages, without intention or fear of another reading it.

Telling Our Own Stories

In bringing more of ourselves into what we do, we are more at ease. When we forget ourselves in the moment, as artists do, we are being, paradoxically, more of ourselves. This is what the stories here tell. This is a vital and a life-enhancing practice.

Vital Practice is successful practice in that by being more ourselves, we free up our vitality. We get out from under the dead weight of what I am calling the *comfort story.*

Comfort stories are those we already know. The story of our lives that makes sense of it. The ones we trot out as anecdotes, explanations, apologies and excuses for what we do and how we are.

The homeopathic and supervisory project is about 'waking up' to our comfort stories and in so doing, giving voice to our more *elemental* ones; to be present to what is really motivating us.

Now these more elemental stories tell us. We don't tell them. These are the stories we don't yet know but that drive us anyway. These are the tales we can observe in body language, sign and symptom. These are the characters that knock on our doors in dreams, that spring to our mouths as metaphor, that write themselves down as poetry or else as uncensored 'morning pages' (exercise above).

These are the stories that begin with listening within.

How do you listen to yourself? What space and time have you for listening to yourself?

Checking in: Get comfortable, somewhere undisturbed and with time enough to spare. Listen to your breath, to the sounds you make, to the posture you hold, to the way your body parts feel, to the tension and the relaxation.

You could try lying on your back on a soft covered floor. Be warm and let your body fall outward. Your ankles flop to the floor, your arms lying a little apart from your sides, your palms turned upwards. You could close your eyes and rest. Let your tongue float up to the roof of your mouth, your lips part just a little.

Now, begin with tensing and then relaxing your body, part by part, ascending from your toes, to your feet, ankles, calves, knees, thighs, buttocks, back, abdomen, chest, shoulders, arms, hands, sides, neck, head, eyes, nose, mouth, face, jaw. Tense and relax. Thoughts come and go. Notice your breath coming and going. Relax. What do you notice? Perhaps you will sleep now. Perhaps the relaxation will refresh you. When you are ready, bring your knees up to your chest and gently rock yourself up into a sitting position. Or you could turn onto your side into the rescue pose and use your arms to raise yourself.

How are you?

What are you really like just now?

Actively listening to ourselves; noticing where we are at ease and where there is something not quite right; something ill at ease. What is it?

In actively listening to ourselves; our bodies, the comfort story is interrupted. This is how a supervisory quality of looking contributes to rapid, gentle and lasting change — in drawing attention to what is really present. Freed from the constraints of the familiar story we are stuck in, we can start to write it in a way that moves us.

Dis-ease and Separation

I am using the term *'Dis-ease'* in this book to indicate an energetic disturbance, with it's unique character, as expressed in the phrase *'I am not myself.'* It is subjectively felt and may or may not be objectively known as disease. Often, a more or less clearly felt sense of being ill at ease predates the emergence of a named disease. (In acute illness, the 'prodromal period.')

'Disease' refers to particular signs, symptoms and tissue changes, commonly associated with a named disease state: fever, sweat and chills associated with influenza for example. These signs and symptoms can be observed and recorded as well as being felt by the sufferer. (Ted Kaptchuck and Michael Croucher, 1986 use the terms 'disease' and 'illness' to make the distinction between observable disease and felt illness.)

When we are healthy, we forget ourselves. We aren't aware of the guts digesting or the leg that walks and climbs without aching. We are at one with ourselves. When we are unhealthy we are restricted in some way; unable to move so freely and unselfconsciously. Perhaps we are stuck in a feeling, or in a fixed idea or a job or relationship that is 'going nowhere.'

In dis-ease or ill at ease, we are separated from ourselves in some way, too. It may be that I am 'beside myself' with severe physical or emotional pain or that a tumor grows separately from my *life force,* grows as it were, without my integrity.

Healing is the Same as Healing Relationship

Dis-ease is separation from ourselves. It is separation of one from another too; of the sick from the healed, the rich from the poor, the enlightened from the unenlightened. We know each of us contain the seeds of the other yet, in adopting the polarity *"I'll be healer and you be healed"* for example, we get fixed at one end and this itself creates dis-ease. Because dis-ease is separation. The question arises, 'Are some people healers and other not?'

Healing is a Self Healing Project

In healing relationship we are developing awareness of our common suffering. We are seeing ourselves in each other; the most obnoxious stranger finds echo in us. We are growing; in awareness, in generosity, in compassion. Our stories are large. We are healing our own divisions. In engaging in healing relationship we are healing ourselves.

If We Follow the Way of Healing We May be Dead First

Healing is not the same as recovering from any particular pathology or relieving any particular symptom or suffering. If we follow the way of healing, we may be dead first. If we want to stay alive, we had better be prepared at times to use all the means at our disposal. We use surgery, medicine, and all our crafty ways, to palliate, to relieve suffering and to prolong life. Where there is life there is potential for healing. When I become my painful knee because I can be aware of little else while it hurts so much, there is little room for wonder, growth or healing. The flip side of art and craft is after all artifice and craftiness.

> "Medicine is a desperate act, and all cures are miracles. Healing works against the deep seated and inevitable fact of disease and

decay. But disease embraces life and is its close ally from the beginning when the fertilizing sperm is little more than a virus to which the egg accedes. Throughout the wondrous transformation that follows, disease is the basis of all the defence mechanisms and immunities that keep this creature alive. The final disease is the 'nigredo' of the original infection. The point is not to evade disease but to keep it integrated with the living. 'Of course it's impossible,' Enslin told us 'Therefore do it.'" (Grossinger, 1980; Enslin, 1977)

Of course it is impossible. And what else will we do if not strive continually to be more at ease; more at one with ourselves and each other? Have we anything better to do after all than attend to our relationships? (Kaplin, 2001)

Suffering is relieved in a variety of ways. Health is restored upon a principled response alone.

In clarifying intention on this point we are at least helped to make what are still nigh impossible judgement calls. (See Chapter Four, 'Ain't Gonna Die for You.')

The Supervisory Way

Carroll (2001, p. 78) refers to *'the supervisory way of life'*.

Impossible judgment calls are what the supervisory project is all about.

"Supervision is a project centered on knowing. Knowledge can be either persecutory or benign." (Balint, 1959)

Balint is reminding us that where there is knowledge there is power. The supervisory voice is the one who is supposed to know. What is the intention in attempting to know what is happening? And how will that knowledge be used? With benign intent to help us to be more aware of our practice? Or to persecute us with superior or harsh judgement?

What story will the supervisor tell? How inclusive will it be? Will it be the supervisor's own story? The practitioner's? The client's? The story of the healing modality? Will it be relevant to all of those? Who will own it?

Clinical supervision is the art of appreciative or compassionate inquiry. What are we inquiring into and in what spirit?

Supervision is a Quality of Looking

Supervision, literally overview, is a quality of looking.

For example, we are generally attached to outcomes:

"I want to feel better."

"I want to prescribe the curative remedy to this patient."

"I want to write this book."

We see ourselves wanting these things. There is a part of us that is looking at the bigger picture; looking at us wanting and looking at how it is:

"I want to get better but I don't want to go to bed when I'm tired."

"I want to give the curative remedy but I don't yet have a clear idea of what the disease is and I don't want to know this because I need to fix it now."

"I want to write this book but I keep taking on more appointments so that I don't have time."

I am referring to supervision as a 'quality of looking' in order to explore the supervisory aspect of relationship in general. Supervision is not to be indifferent to outcomes so much as to cultivate a curiosity about what is really happening; a curiosity which may become with practice greater motivation than our defence of what we should like to see happen. Cultivating this curiosity brings us up against all of our most cherished beliefs,values, defences and strongly held positions.

An Inclusive Approach — Person to Practice Centred

In person-centred terms (Carl Rogers, 1961, p. 20), the supervisory quality of looking is akin to 'unconditionally accepting' or 'positively regarding' another. (See Hahnemann, 1842, Aphorism 6, Unprejudiced Observation.) For an insightful and meticulously researched account of the similarities between the person centred approach and homeopathy see to Ian Thompson (2004):

> "Neither person-centred practice nor homeopathy seeks to guide or influence the individual's growth. In both cases, practitioners attempt to provide *'unconditional positive regard'* or an *'unprejudiced observer'* (homeopathy) and are equally concerned to understand the interior meaning of the individual's experiencing: the homeopth carefully listening to the individual's story is as concerned to grasp the individual's *'internal frame of reference'* as is the person-centred therapist."

The significance of the person centred view seems to me to be particularly in relationship to power in the helping and healing professions. Pre-dating developments in reflective practice, it can be seen in the light of a formative response to the all-consuming power of the 'expert' to author our stories for us. The person centred practitioner surrenders their way to follow the momentum of the other. An inclusive or practice centred approach suggests that momentum is continually recreated in the encounter. The question is 'what is happening here and here and here to increase awareness of what is being presented?' (see pp. 67-68).

Dynamic Supervision

Add 'dynamic' to this inquiry and we get an attempt to perceive the essential or energetic nature of what is happening 'here and now' — What is moving and how? Dynamis is the force that moves us.

"What is here now?"

"What does it look like?"

"Feel like?"

"Where is it located between us?"

"What is its nature?"

"Form?"

"How does it move?"

"What is the direction, pace and quality of the movement?"

Supervision inquires into what isn't noticed at the time because it happens too quickly, is on the edge of awareness or else is cloaked in the dead weight of the *comfort story* — that which we already know and prevents us from learning anew. (See Chapter One, 'What is the Matter?' Chapter Two, 'Let's Go Fly a Kite,' Chapter Three, 'Cheetah.')

Being willing and able to inquire into 'what is' rather than what we should like to see is a vital practice. It focuses on what is important; the continual movement within and between us. What shape are we making? What is the pattern?

Dynamic Practice and Creativity

Creativity is more and other than a method we can bring to practice to liven it up from time to time. More than remembering to bring the right brain into an essentially left brained activity. Creativity is the essence of practice.

Dynamic practice implies an ongoing conversation between right and left brain. If we are practicing any healing art then we are in the act of creation. When we inquire into the dynamics of practice, that is do supervision, we are re-creating practice anew. Every moment is a new opportunity to re-create patterns, to see in a new light, to tilt the glass…

Reflective to Dynamic Practice

Elektra Tselikas-Portman in *Supervision and Dramatherapy* says:

> "In a culture that bases professional activity on rational thinking, that believes in and propagates the power of reflection for the gaining of insight and growth, the question arises: in which way does such a process help the professional cope with the demands of her professional situations?" (p. 27)

She goes on to say

> "The artistic creation… allows a contact with the depths, a sounding that expands perception, puts us in contact with imagination and allows us to feed the soul, see with many eyes, speak many languages, particularly those which are beyond linguistic constructions." [Like the language of disease.]

The reflective practitioner is one aspect of our artistic selves; the Apollonian side, bringing up into the light of consciousness what is shadowed. The Dionysian; the depths where dis-easing grows, requires of us quite another willingness; to let go of understanding, to fall down into the chaos, to not see what is happening in order to experience anew.

The term *'reflective practitioner'* is a later development in response to the predominant professional mode of *'expert practitioner,'* the seminal work comimg twenty years after Rogers (1961). (Schon, 1983). The polarity is between the one who is presumed to know and the other who is willing to find out.

I prefer the term dynamic practitioner and *dynamic practice* now in that it refers us to the continual movement between light and dark; conscious control and motive forces. It includes reflection and goes onto movement. It encompasses creative ways; what I am calling 'art-play,' as a natural part of the practitioner's art rather than an optional add on. It refers us to the energetic nature of healing and dis-easing.

Healing and Learning — Get in Role and on Task

A healing practice intends that we should 'forget' ourselves and be well and go on. When we are well we don't notice ourselves. We don't remember ourselves. We aren't self conscious. We are and we do. A dynamic supervision is 'waking up' to the reality of our practice. The intention is to remember and learn. In seeing it how it is, we are helped let go of unrealistic expectations and delusions: the delusion that we are either healers or to be healed, for example?

When we go to a practitioner we learn something valuable about ourselves and our lives. The actively listening therapist who is present to us, enables us to hear ourselves. We see it how it is. We get supervision in other words. Sometimes when we go to supervision, the quality of attention allows us to recover ourselves. We stop 'beating ourselves up' or getting ourselves 'stuck' in practice. We 'forget' what the problem was and move on. We can act. We are healed so to speak.

Healing relationship happens everywhere. Learning too. Intention is what counts. We come to a practitioner of the healing arts intending to recover our ability to adapt, survive and thrive. We come to supervision intending to learn afresh what is happening. No-one thanks a supervisor for pathologising our vulnerability or a practitioner for unwanted insights when we just want to get better.

When we set up a supervisory relationship, we give ourselves specific roles and tasks — to supervise and to be supervised, to inquire and to learn.

Defining terms

Role

We meet as people. We adopt the *role* of 'practitioner,' 'supervisor,' 'patient' or 'client.' Together we make a relationship. We make the *case* for what the matter is together. A more or less healing response arises between us. It depends upon the art and skill of the healing artist. It depends upon the nature of the dis-ease. It depends upon the intention of the client or patient. It depends too upon the quality of the relationship in which the art is practiced. (Ryan, 2002)

We do role play in supervision to wake us up to the nature and tasks of each role. We do it to notice fixity in staying in one role. Role play *(art-play)* encourages practicing with ease in moving freely between roles. (See 'Vital Kit, Guides for Triading.')

Task

Every relationship and role has its tasks: (Carroll, 1996, Ch. 4 for supervision tasks) the therapeutic relationship to recover health and well being; freedom to move . The teacher to teach; the student to learn; the supervisor to inquire into practice in the interests of client welfare, practitioner awareness and development of the healing or helping modality.

Getting in role and staying on task is an ethical practice. We come to know what we can expect. We are made aware that this is a formal space; a heightened atmosphere where we intend something to happen, something to move. This is more and other than a 'chat' or 'tea and sympathy.' This is a rare and focused relationship in which anything can happen. Everyday miracles.

Intention is everything.

"What do I intend in being in this relationship?"

"What is my task?"

"What competence, qualities and skills do I need?"

"What do I expect?" (See 'Vital Kit, Working Relationships' C.E.P. — Competency, Expectation and Process model.)

Supervision Mentoring and Coaching — Roles and Tasks

These are terms often used interchangeably — context is everything. In clinical and therapeutic practices, supervision refers to a collegiate, compassionate and independent inquiry into practice for the benefit of the practitioner or group in supervision. The intention is to benefit the practice and the helping or healing modality as a whole, restoring the practitioner to autonomy and relatedness. The supervisor in turn is supervised for her clinical practice as well as for her role as supervisor. This is not the same as managerial supervision in which one worker is answerable to another in a hierarchical structure.

The emphasis in this collection is on supervision as a quality of looking as I have said: an appreciative or a compassionate inquiry; a way of observing without attachment. In this sense, a supervisory way belongs to any relationship — therapeutic, professional helping, mentoring, teaching, parenting or marriage as well as to self supervising. Any relationship can benefit from a supervisory way of looking.

A mentor implies someone who has gone before; a more seasoned traveler along the way; one who can *model* for us how to make the journey and show us where the next step might be. In professional terms, a mentor inducts us into the mores, values and ways of the professional community. They show us the ropes. The word 'mentor' originates with the story of Telemachus, son of the wandering Odysseus, who was guided by Mentor.

In fact though, mentoring is as often a relationship between people of very different professions and across business-professional-personal boundaries, so that a head teacher may be mentored by a supermarket manager for example. This emphasizes the 'quality of looking' rather than experience in a particular field as the working definition of mentorship in use here. The art is in noticing the similarities and differences at an essential, a motivational level, even though the fields may seem superficially quite different.

A supervisor may well be a more experienced practitioner, a mentor, for her supervisees, and needs to be so in the case of student and fledgling practitioners. Mentorship, as more experienced guide, will be an aspect of some supervisory relationships. When it comes to peer supervision, mentorship tends to play less of a role. We may even choose a less experienced person to supervise us, since it is the quality of their attention we are after as much as, or more than, their experience of our healing modality.

A coach relates to performance of specific skills, tasks and goals. Coaching may then be an aspect of a supervisory, a mentoring or other helping relationship. We may at any time have specific needs for coaching. What is our own coaching style? What can we each coach another to do? How much of our parenting, supervising and mentoring is coaching in its emphasis? Where is coaching an appropriate response to the relationship under inquiry? Teaching clearly involves coaching — it also involves supervising and mentoring.

Confused? Where a *mentor* implies guidance, a *supervisor* is more likely to observe, question and reflect. A *coach* is more likely to be performance and goal oriented. It is a matter of emphasis and context. The terms are used interchangeably and this can mean we lose the specific words we need to describe different aspects of helping relationship.

The Homeopathic Way

This book comes from my practice of homeopathy. This is my art. I practice every day. It is a practice, not a perfect. I do it. This is my profession. I profess it aloud. I practice 'being' homeopathic as much as I 'do' homeopathy. It is this being homeopathic that interests me here — what difference does it make to anything? How does it contribute to healing relationship? What is it anyway?

Homeopathy, like counselling and psycho-therapy, is a narrative art. In common with these, we bring stories of our lives, loves, hopes, fears, *dis-ease* and *diseases*. Unlike some, though not all other forms of narrative therapy, homeopathy responds remedially to physical expressions of suffering as well as to mental, emotional and soul sickness.

Homeopathy is a principled response. These principles are simple, universal, profound and mysterious — making them just about right then for the riddle of healing and diseasing.

Homeopathy belongs to three traditions and is based upon three observations (as good stories are).

The three traditions are the vitalistic, hermetic and empirical: See to Misha Norland (2003) for an account both vital and sufficient.

Just a taste of these universal stories here to orient us through the tales that follow:

Vitalism

While we are more or less healthy we are on the move; free to change our hearts and minds. Health and disease originate vitally; the source cannot be found in discrete organs or systems. *Dis-easing*, literally becoming ill at ease, is in some way before and other than organ- or system-specific *disease*. Long before the tissues register discrete changes, we are not so free as we could be: We either don't remember when things started to go wrong... or we remember we were never well since... and we can't get back to how it was before...

This vital or dynamic aspect of the relationship is what we are focusing on. The 'vital' questions for relationship are:

How is the relationship moving?

What is the quality of the motion?

In what direction are we going and at what pace?

What moves or motivates the relationship?

What obstacles are in the way of its free movement?

Hermeticism

Homeopathy is concerned with the latent properties of things. This is an aspect of its hermetic root:

> "The silver of silver, the gold of gold, the sulphur of sulphur"
> (Richard Grossinger, 1980)

The hermetic tradition is concerned with conveying the hidden and unifying principle of matter. How do all the different elements unite to express its peculiar character?

> "Everything in creation, man and medicines included, has a visible and an invisible aspect, a limited outer form and an unbounded inner spirit. The outer form can be known by observation with our ordinary senses. The inner spirit can be sensed by intuition." (Norland, 2003)

The stories in this book explore the power of *metaphor* or analogy to communicate the essence of a thing. A remedy prescribed homeopathically is in this sense a metaphor for dis-ease. It is *like* the dis-ease in its action. While it may be a wildly different thing; a salmon, a *Thuja* tree, silver or gold, its quality is similar to the distinct features of the dis-ease it describes. It moves in a similar way. Every remedy comes as a story, told through *potentisation, provings* and clinical cases. We could say homeopathy is story as healing art. (See to stories 'What is the Matter?' 'Cheetah.' 'Waking Up to the Dream' for more on this.)

Gold (*Aurum*), a remedy known to the ancients and used *allopathically* today for its local action in some arthritic conditions, reveals itself through *trituration, potentisation* and *provings*. It is characterized, whatever the local complaint; heart disease, glandular, bone or skin disease, by a movement away from life, love and community and towards despair.

> "We say 'homeopathic gold' because gold when tested on normal, healthy persons has produced just such states of suicidal despair and hopelessness; and again, because by its reduction to infinitesimals the noble metal, thrice noble in these its higher uses, (higher potencies) emerges from bulk, weight, visibility and inertness, as a mighty energy to strengthen the will and revive the natural affections — even to the deepest and most fundamental of all — the LOVE OF LIFE." (M. Tyler, 1952)

We could say, with Parry and Doan, who call all narrative therapies *"clinical hermeneutics"* (A. Parry & R. Doan, 1994) that we are everywhere engaged in hermeneutics as we seek to interpret the world according to our own lights. For a person in an *Aurum* state, that phone not ringing must always mean friends have forsaken him. That is the essence of the thing for him.

The 'essential' questions for relationship are:

What is the essence of this relationship?

What is it characterized by?

What is the story we are co-creating?

What would a metaphor for it be?

Empiricism

Homeopathy has grown directly out of treatment of the sick. It is in the empirical tradition, based upon sense experience.

> "Many ancient systems of healing, including the Indian Ayurvedic system and the shamanistic traditions, stress the need to develop the powers of observation and intuition — the outward and inward eye — in order to get to know the visible and invisible aspects of medicinal substances." (Norland, 2003)

The homeopathic agent of change, the potentised remedy, is *proved* by a group of people recording its effects over time. The 'as if one' story of each remedy thus proved, is compiled by a proving conductor, whose role is akin to a group supervisor. (Sherr, 1994) The scientific explanation of homeopathy is not yet complete. That it does restore the sick to health, time and again, is known from experience.

Just as Seurat's pointillism prefigured the pixel, potentisation points to a future scientific understanding of the relationship between energy and matter. And just as the science of colour does not explain art, neither will the science of potentised remedies explain homeopathy and healing.

Homeopathy is an empirical practice born of necessity.

The 'empirical' questions for relationship are:

What is happening here?

What is the sense of it?

What is the experience?

Homeopathy is Based Principally upon Three Observations

1. The unique story.

Health and disease are unique to each individual. We each have our own susceptibility as well as sharing common vulnerability. (I may be vulnerable to drafts. We are all sensitive to lack of clean water.) It follows that we all see from our unique vantage point. In that sense, there is nothing outside of ourselves. I am vulnerable to drafts so that when you close that door it must be because you too are vulnerable to drafts and not because you are sensitive to noise as is actually the case.

2. The story of correspondence.

Vital disease is cured by a vital and similar stimulus. This is the law of correspondence 'beautifully expressed by the Romantic poet Blake as a universe in a grain of sand.' (Norland, 2003) Homeopathy means literally 'Like cures like.' An allopath generally treats the manifestations of disease. 'Allo' meaning other. To do other than is already being done. If the body inflames give an anti-inflammatory. If a bacteria is found at the same time as an inflammation, give an anti-biotic, literally an anti-life. To respond homeopathically is to get alongside what is happening and do something similar to it, and do it in potency; energetically. The Belladonna plant has the ability to cause inflammation, and, given in a vital and minimum dose, to cure it too. In homeopathy, a 'dis-ease' is diagnosed in naming the remedy. The diagnosis is the remedy. In *allopathy* naming the 'disease' is just the beginning of looking for the cure.

3. The story of the minimum dose.

A minimum, vital and similar stimulus only is required to restore well being.

"Yin and Yang are in constant flux. Change is inevitable. According to Newton's third law of thermodynamics, every action has an equal and opposite reaction." (Norland, 2003). To offer a minimal push in the direction already taken means that the movement will inevitably come back the other way — so gently support the body's attempt to rid infection by raising a fever, in offering a *potentised* dose of a remedy that can itself cause fever.

In Summary

- Dis-ease originates vitally. Therefore the response needs to be vital or dynamic as in a *potentised remedy.*

- The course of dis-easing depends upon unique susceptibility.

- A minimum intervention in the direction already taken stimulates a healing response.

A remedy chosen according to these simple principles is instrumental in restoring health. The stories here ask "Are they not also guides for healing, or we might call it, 'right,' relationship?"

A Homeopathic Way of Relating?

If the origins of disease are vital, this is the same as saying they begin in our relationships; with ourselves, each other and the environment. If we can attend to right relationship, we are doing healing and we are doing preventative medicine. We are looking after ourselves, each other, and the planet too.

- Each relationship is unique.
- The energetic or vital quality of a relationship is what is healing; the quality of 'being' rather than 'doing.'
- The quality of a healing relationship is characterized by *getting alongside* and by *minimum intervention.*

A Homeopathic Way of Supervising?

- Each supervisory and practice relationship is unique.
- What is happening? In practice? Here in supervision? What are we being for each other? What are we making together? What story are we telling?
- What is the minimum intervention that 'gets alongside' the practitioner in supervision to restore them to autonomy and relatedness ?

A Supervisory Way of Doing Homeopathy?

- What is happening?
- How do I perceive it in the 'here and now'?
- How do I accept it unconditionally?

The stories unfold in a manner vitalistic, hermetic and empirical. Stories reveal the energetic nature in a way no amount of talking *about* an event can. They get to the essence in metaphor and allusion. They take a real event and convey it to us by asking us to sense, imagine, intuit and reflect upon it. Stories touch us. And when we are touched we move...

STORIES FROM THE HEALING ARTS

The Healing Art of Story

I magine a life without stories; those we tell to make sense of our lives, the threads we weave between us, our family and nation stories, history as story. We inhabit a world of story-telling and myth-making. Stories bear witness to our lives. In a real sense, we never get outside them. We work hard to fit what happens into them, only changing the tale when push comes to shove.

What a thought. You fitting me into your version and me shoving you into mine. What a time we have getting to know each other! (1st and 2nd Order Cybernetics, Parry and Doan, 1994. p. 24)

Homeopathy is a narrative therapy. Our knowledge of remedies prescribed homeopathically come from the collective story of the participants in a remedy *proving*.

People come to tell their stories and to be listened to.

The homeopath in turn, retells the story as a remedy narrative — delivered in potency.

A supervisor, or supervisory aspect of self, is concerned with the stories we tell in practice: Clients bring stories. A 'case' is a practitioner's story about a client or patient. Every healing modality comes with its own stories, including maps and traditions.

Supervision is the process by which we re-write the stories we are 'stuck' in. In attending to the 'bigger stories,' our universal ones, the supervisory quality of looking helps us to see where we have been and where we might go next.

Paradoxically then, the more experience we get in our field the more we need the supervisory quality of witness. Only an 'outsider' perspective can keep the bigger picture in view once we are steeped in the stories we make of our relationships and professions.

Of course the supervisor comes complete with narratives too…

It is in the spirit of appreciative inquiry, albeit with the understanding that observation is always participant, that we hear the faint echo of the *elemental story* in the familiarity of those *comfort (or discomfort) stories* we tell ourselves.

Comfort stories make sense of who we are, what we are doing, where we have been and where we are going. The elemental story is concerned with what really moves us whether we like the idea of it or not. This story is told to an *active listener* or to that actively listening part of ourselves that is more interested in finding out how it is and how it might be than is attached to it being any particular way; the supervising or witnessing self. The conflict between curiosity and defending the comfort story is at the heart of supervision and practice.

The inquirers we bring to the task need be both safe and risky enough to hold the inquiry; neither too coddling nor persecuting. Working with the level of mistrust is at the heart of supervisory practice.

Without such compassionate inquiry, our stories can be taken away from us and translated in terms which bear little relation to our lived experience: Medicine, for example, even alternatives to conventional practices, can author our stories for us; tidying up loose ends in diagnoses, interpretations, palliations and 'cures' that leave us feeling there is yet something amiss. (See to story of Reich in Grossman, 1980, p. 275)

"The meaning of our lives is still unfolding" Alice Walker chants (Walker, 1985) and yet we are fixing ourselves as this and that all the time as if movement were no longer a possibility.

"I am arthritic," "I am depressed," " I am an addict."

Even changing the words to

"I am doing arthritis," " I am doing depression," " I am doing addiction"

reminds us there is the possibility of *not* doing them.

'A disabled person' fixes the disability as belonging to the person. 'A person with a disability' begs the question,

"Whose disability is it? The person's or society's?" Language is important. Telling our stories in our own words is to author our own lives.

Getting alongside the experience of the patient; letting them tell their own tale, is explored in the first story in this collection, 'What Is the Matter?' The patient here is finding out the differences between her 'comfort' stories; the ones she already knows, and the more 'elemental' one she has yet to discover. The practitioner's simple act of listening to what is present allows the inquiry to unfold.

We tell our elemental stories in action more than words. The body does what the mind won't allow.

The second story, 'Let's Go Fly a Kite,' explores a practice essentially without words. Here a group of adults with learning difficulties are encouraged to take on a hugely difficult physical task in an attempt to wake them up to their own experience. The focus becomes not so much the story narrated in words, as the unspoken quality of healing relationship. A homeopathic way of relating is explored. The vital arts of *actively listening* to what is happening and *art-play* are exercised here.

We make our stories together. We affect each other. How we relate to each other is at the heart of ethical practice. It isn't enough to just tell the story differently in order to move and change. Stories are co-created. They represent power struggle and vested interests. We do the best we can in telling our stories. Comfort stories make the best of bad situations. Let us not rob ourselves of our comfort stories where we cannot move. But where we can…

In group supervisions we get the bigger picture. We see more clearly where we can move and where we cannot. It isn't just the benefit of bringing more talking heads to a difficult *case*. In working dynamically, we create a group story that itself parallels or re-creates, as microcosm, the whole intra-psychic, relational, social and political world of the situation we want to explore.

The third story, 'Cheetah,' takes the leap from reflective to dynamic practice in re-creating a patient-practitioner story in dramatic action. Tracking down the story of a group supervision, we see the cheetah emerge from the shadows. In he stalks, hunting his own children as prey. In creating an *aesthetic distance* **from the case in this way, the practitioner realizes there are no 'stuck cases.' There are never any stuck cases — although that is how we most often present the issue in supervision — it is always** *we* **who get stuck. The 'case' is always what it is. The practitioner moves from a stuck place to standing her own ground, and in so doing, releases the patient...**

Our stories show us, we are not the 'arrived,' the 'healed,' but fellow sufferers with as little knowledge and certainty as the next person. Practitioners are not perfect — Let's drop the perfect parent, teacher, supervisor, healer and keep practicing!

A vital practice makes no distinction of merit between the art of healing and the craft of relieving suffering. Awareness of what it is we are doing holds faith with ourselves and with our patients. This is life enhancing for both practitioner and patient.

We are well named practitioners of the healing arts. A practitioner must do. Art needs be practiced.

We practice an art; whether it be the art of parenting, helping or healing; any art of relationship between people is a daily practice of communicating with the healing archetypes.

> "There are no healers; there are only those through whom the healer archetype works, through whom Apollo and Dionysus speak." (James Hillman, 1965)

Golden Apollo who stands in the light of consciousness. Dark Dionysus who hides in the shadows.

> "As in the fairy tale, at this stage (the mythological or imaginal) opposites are inclusive, not exclusive... A figure can be both here and absent, past and present, self and not self, dead and yet alive simultaneously. Mice can turn into horses, a pumpkin into a coach. This resembles the dream state in which soul becomes aware of itself and converses with itself, as it were, in terms of imaginal emotion-reasoning." (Whitmont, 1983)

We are concerned with polarities between health and dis-ease, healer and sufferer, rational and irrational, conscious and unconscious, body and mind, as inclusive rather than exclusive elements. The one will get into the other. (See Chapter Seven, 'The Dog's Story.') It is ancient myth, legend and fairy tale, as well as modern provings of potentised remedies, that speak of these archetypal states in inclusive ways. So it is the art both of story telling and listening to story that is explored here in order to gain insight into healing relationship which is itself an inclusive affair. Who is healed and who is doing the healing? The one will get into the other.

James Hillman again:

"The art of healing is the healing of art."

Dedicating ourselves to our art, living for our art is that our urgent and passionate task?

When we are freely practicing our art the dance is towards the light even as we turn and face into the dark. We feel compassion. We experience practice as interesting, energizing and inspirational. Even as we struggle and lose faith, trip over ourselves, make fools of ourselves, and stand by helplessly, we come back for more practice the next day. We are doing our art and that is our task. And that is compassionate medicine.

The tales we tell are epic ones; fantastical, unique, heroic and universal — tales to connect us to the heavens above and the seas below.

The fourth story, 'Ain't Gonna Die For You,' follows a group supervision of a practitioner struggling with the experience of a patient who develops a life-threatening disease while in his care. His compassion for the patient, his skill as a practitioner and his ability to look after himself are each challenged and confronted. In finding his voice through the group's singing, chanting and drumming, Sam recovers his compassion. *Art-play*, the collective story and the group as a dynamic force for change are celebrated in this story.

Many of us feel *burnt out* at times by the demands of helping. (Ram Dass & Gorman, 1986) Disconnected from our own creative life force, even while we are helping others to develop or recover theirs. We may start out learning anew each day and soon find that a deadly routinism is creeping in to replace the dynamic rituals we set out with. We may try to fix this by devouring new teachers, books, maps and models, only to find that they fall apart in our hands. What are we making of our own experience even as we are informed by another's? Where is our own inspiration and passionate inquiry?

What is our own story?

The fifth story, 'Magic Glasses,' explores the stories we tell ourselves about who we are and what we are capable of. How it is we 'dis-member' and then 're-member' ourselves. It acknowledges the loss incurred in letting go of one version of events, the way we are attached to being, in favour of telling a more realistic tale, of how it is and might be. It asks the question: "How available am I to myself and therefore to anyone I am working with?"

We truly meet each other at the level we meet ourselves. In that sense, there is nothing outside of ourselves. The healing relationship is a self healing one.

Just as we bring different voices to our story telling, we listen in different ways. The Acupuncturist listens to the story the meridians tell. The Jungian therapist to the archetypal stories written in the individual life. The homeopath to the story of correspondences.

How do we listen? *"I hear you"* we say when we mean our ears are open but our hearts and minds are closed to what is being said.

Active listening is quite different from passively hearing or even from ordinary listening. When we listen actively we are engaging our full attention; senses, hearts and minds. We intend to listen. And to what?

We are listening to ourselves listening to the other.

We are listening to the space in between us; to what we are making between us.

We are listening to the story that can't be said right out.

We are bringing our whole selves to the act of listening.

In narrative therapies, we are actively listening for the clues to the 'elemental' story. We are not so much listening to the story we tell ourselves that makes fixed sense of our lives; our 'comfort' stories. It is the way in which we tell them that reveals something of the elemental story, hence the narrative therapist's focus on original language; the poetry we each bring to our speech.

"I am a survivor of incest," "A person afflicted by M.E,"

"A broken hearted lover," "A searcher after spiritual truth."

Even these common phrases come with their own unique action — 'surviving,' 'afflicting,' 'breaking,' 'questing.'

The sixth story, 'And the Boat Capsized in Deep Waters' explores relationship as meeting between two 'strangers' talking different languages. It focuses on metaphor as the moving line — a link between the *comfort* and the *elemental* story and between one language and another. The power and the tyranny of metaphor are investigated in a recording and commentary on a one-to-one supervision.

Power in the healing and supervisory relationship is confronted here. Whose story is it anyway?

The story that connects us to the bigger story of life and that yet retains the unique patterning of the individual is where the action is.

The questions are the same for the active listener whatever the context:

What is the elemental story? What is the motive force?

With eyes and ears wide open to the as yet unrevealed story, we practice our healing art. Dionysus representing the walk in the dark in unknown territory and Apollo the enlightenment the maps and models bring to what is found there.

The seventh story, 'The Dog's Story,' refers to supervision as a quality of looking; one that wakes us up to what is happening. The chapter introduces the concept of *e-motion* to refer to the elemental way in which we move towards and away from what we need in order to survive and thrive. It relates to body language and to symptom making.

At this 'e-motional' level, we all speak the same language.

Since stories are an aural tradition, you might like to try reading them out loud to yourself or to another. Let them tell you what they are.

Nothing shifts just talking about it… so let the stories begin to tell it.

WHAT IS THE MATTER?

A Patient's Story

CHAPTER ONE

Riding along in my old VW beetle, I throw another full pack of cigarettes out the window. It's the only way I know how to quit smoking. I have told myself it's a waste of money and that I am wasting my health. I have been smoking 20 to 40 a day for ten years with a good dose of bronchitis every winter. Each time I inhale I feel a pulse of pain in my bandaged right knee. I am 27 years old. I use pain killers and steroids sometimes. Regular antibiotics come with itchy thrush. Parking is a nightmare. If I don't get close enough to this office, I might not be able to make the walk. I have come to the homeopath to see what she can do.

She is sitting beside a big desk in a book-lined study. She doesn't get up. She doesn't examine my knee right away. She asks me

"Why here ?" And "Why now ?"

I tell her I am at my wit's end. I have tried this, that and the other and I can't stop smoking. I tell her I buy huge quantities of cigarettes since I have a pact with myself, every time I smoke one I must throw the rest away. I am hoping that the sheer waste will drive me to quit.

"What is wasting?" she asks?

"I am" I say without thinking.

"I am wasting away, weak and wasting my time, wasting my life. Trying this and that, never happy, never content. I am wasting everything. I can't bear waste."

I falter and come to a full stop.

Then I hear myself and I think *Don't waste our time. Tell her what the matter is.*

I remember a story I have told many times, a long time ago now, to many doctors. It begins when I am 10 years old. I am in the office of the school nurse. She is studying my reaction to a skin test to assess need for the BCG, inoculation against tuberculosis. She calls the doctor to have a look. They decide to vaccinate.

This tale is only partly about vaccination for that is another story. This is about the stories we tell ourselves, the ones we know, the *comfort stories,* and the ones hidden beneath the surface ready to interrupt our cosy narratives and reveal a whole new world of meaning and mystery to us.

Ten days after the BCG inoculation my knees hurt. They are so stiff and painful I can't walk very easily. I am kept off school. I go with my mother to the doctors, the hospital, the consultant, the surgeon, the pharmacist.

I tell my story everywhere. Is it a story? That BCG and my stiff knees are somehow related?

"Can't be." "Co-incidence." "No story here." I'm told.

I forget that story in time. I no longer tell it. I say I have rheumatism instead. And that's a different story.

Now, in the homeopath's consulting room, I tell it again, except it comes out differently this time. It is as if it isn't mine. I'm not telling the story so much as it is telling me. I'm not at all sure what will come out of my mouth next. I tell her about what happens after the BCG sure enough. I am on certain ground there. This memory holds true. It is what happens next I'm not sure about.

There is no wave of the hand as if brushing flies as she tells me this is irrelevant. She simply writes down what I have told her and then looks up expectantly for more. It is as if I am free falling. I don't know what next. I have never got further than the BCG story.

"What is happening at ten years old when your knees start aching?" She wonders.

"I don't have to kneel in church any more. I am excused. I no longer genuflect at the alter" is what pops out of my mouth.

And I am delighted at the connection, except I really cannot kneel anymore. I can't run either and I used to be a sprinter. I can see my sketch book; pencil drawings of running knees I am intending to carve. I feel sad and self pitying suddenly; wanting to fix in stone, childish running knees going nowhere.

"I am going nowhere."

I say

"And I want to go everywhere. Time is running out. I knock my head against the wall the headaches are so bad. I stay in bed for three days with menstrual cramps. I wash distalgesics down with red wine to take the throb out of my knees, which is a joke because red wine hurts my knees— except it doesn't — no connection there either apparently." I say with sarcasm.

I am beginning to hear the story. I want to go everywhere and I am going nowhere. I have fixed myself to make sure I can't. What on earth am I afraid of?

The homeopath doesn't appear to do much and just enough. She stays with me as the tale unfolds. She keeps me on my track. She accepts my story and she takes it more seriously than I do in questioning what it is.

She prescribes a single white pill. It is the remedy *Tuberculinum Bovinum* in the 1M potency.

That month I have no headache or pains with my period. Both knees are constantly painful. I am walking with the aid of sticks. I am also writing every day. I am remembering my story, picking up the pieces, following a thread. I am finding bright beads of memory, connecting one event with another, noticing the pattern, the themes.

The rheumatism is not *caused* by the BCG though it seems it may well have been a trigger. That old story needs revising. The patterning of my disease is meaningful in the context of a whole life; headaches, menstrual pain, rheumatic knees, connect one to the other as in the old song,

"The thigh bone connects to the knee bone…"

It is as if they are metaphors for something I can't contact in any other way.

I am getting interested…

I had wanted to be a priest; a vocation closed to Roman Catholic girls. I had been angry with the church for seeming to come between me and my God. The stiff knees certainly meant I no longer bowed my knee in church. A 'tomboy'; painful menses reminded me monthly of the 'curse' of being female. I banged my head against the wall of fixed things I couldn't change.

And this of course is just another story, albeit a simplified one for the sake of telling. It certainly speaks to some of my experience since, when 'the story' is given to me in *potency,* as a homeopathic remedy, it restores some freedom to move: I can get out of bed during a period and I can write with a clear head (*Hering's Law*).

It takes another 15 years and more stories, before I pick up my knees to run again. I run every morning now. Not far. I am a sprinter.

I wasn't given the remedy *Tuberculinum* because a BCG inoculation caused my symptoms. I was given it because it mirrors my story.

I was already susceptible to *Tuberculinum,* before the BCG. My uncles both had tuberculosis, that is a part of it. Listen to another part taken from the *provings* as well as from clinical experience of the remedy *Tuberculinum.*

The Story of *Tuberculinum*

'"The Lost Homeland

The Tuberculinum nosode is associated in a homeopath's mind with restless discontent. It is derived from a disease that arises in dispossessed populations and societies. People who have experienced this tragedy feel as if their heart is stuck in the record groove of the past and is singing the song of longing for the lost homeland: they are always looking for it, comparing the new against the old and finding the new wanting. Therefore, we find them restlessly searching for (but not finding) a new home and culture." (Norland, 2003)

The conflict in this patient's story is between being 'exiled' from her childhood religious culture and desiring to escape from what she experiences as oppressive constraints of it. She is moving on but to what? This is Rajan Sankaran (1994)

> "Jurgen Becker sees the theme of *Tuberculinum* in the fairy tale of Red Riding Hood. Riding Hood is the young girl who has been told by her mother to walk along the straight path (and no other) in order to reach her grandmother's place. She is warned that if she deviates from this path, she might lose her way and get into trouble. The wolf tempts her to leave the path and try a different one — it promises excitement instead of monotony. Riding Hood takes her chance and, as we know, the wolf reaches the grandmother and eats her up before Riding Hood finds her way to the cottage."

In showing the remedy as fairy tale or legend as in 'The Lost Homeland,' several things are accomplished:

We are reminded of the essence of the story by connecting it to one we have ingested with our mother's milk, the story of Irish exile due to potatoe famine and religious persecution for example. Many myths and fairy tales may remind us of a state or remedy. In choosing one, we make connection with a bigger picture of human being and human doing. The work of Jan Scholten, in plotting the elements of the periodic table in relation to stages in heroic journeying, is in this tradition. (J. Scholten, 1996)

Always remembering, that in choosing one connection we are discarding another. The map is not after all, as we say, the territory.

In connecting the remedy *Tuberculinum* with Little Red Riding Hood or the story of exile, we connect with the inner journey as well as with the socially rebellious aspect.

Our universal stories of growing up, rebellion against our elders and social norms are characterised thus for *Tuberculinum*: The grass is always greener on the other side. Wandering from the path is mirrored in the wandering joint pains that are better for continual motion. Symptoms change continually, each beginning and ending suddenly. The motion of *Tuberculinum* is throughout one of restless change without arriving so that in the end there is wasting away. That is its signature.

It is the signature too of the inner journey.

The archetypal heroic journey is invoked by the story of Red Riding Hood: Becoming more of ourselves, finding our own way of being. 'Red' refers us to the alchemical map of psychic transformation; the 'rubedo.' Red is the colour of sacrifice so that new life can come. Red Riding Hood is in this way a story of giving birth to the self.

In this state a person is wandering from the path to find their own way. Red Riding Hood is tempted to follow her own primal nature in the body of the wolf. Old knowledge, in the person of the grandmother, is then eaten up by her quest.

"What big eyes you have," she says and *"What a big mouth." "All the better to eat you with,"* replies her wild wolf self.

Thus at the end of the journey, when Red Riding Hood has seen what she has seen of her own nature and made the journey from innocence to mature sexuality, the old knowledge is restored to her. Her grandmother is freed from the wolf by the woodcutter, who slices him open with his axe. This is the version of the story I remember from childhood. There are of course very many variations.

In ancient matriarchal religion the axe is a symbol of initiation. The woodcutter prunes the saplings to promote strong growth. In this fairy story, layered over old women's religious myths, it is the woodsman rather than a Goddess who frees Red Riding Hood from her unconscious animal and sexual nature, restoring her both to the old wisdoms of her sex and renewed consciousness of herself.

Tuberculinum is one version of a universal story; the psyche's attempt to integrate its own divided nature. Red Riding Hood is one metaphor for the *Tuberculinum* state — one we might remember since it is a fairy tale.

The legend of 'The lost homeland' also refers us to exile from old ways to make our own psychic journeys.

In Red Riding Hood, animal nature in the body of the wolf reminds us that healing and *dis-easing* are primal activities; that we need to go deep into the stories we tell ourselves to reach more basic drives. (See Chapter Seven, 'The Dog's Story.') Presence to the moment reveals the expressions of the elemental story. It isn't a matter of interpretation or of delving into the past for its own sake. These stories come in later to make sense of what is revealed.

Tuberculinum, in the body of the remedy is a metaphor so to speak, capturing the essence of the state of restless dis-integration. It is itself a story. And stories are themselves a healing art.

Narrative therapists and in turn their supervisors are asking:

How does the person tell their story of what the matter is?

What is their elemental story? How is it told?

What, literally, is the matter that answers?

What is its story?

Tuberculinum tells the tale of restless searching. In this case it meets the wandering rheumatic pains, the painful menses and the insistent headaches induced by frustrated journeying without arriving. The homeopathic patient in this story is wasting away. The remedy meets her at an optimum moment. There is no time to waste.

Stories in general lift us out of isolated experience of suffering and unknowing, connecting us with a shared experience of living and making meanings.

Metaphorical stories, words and phrases, like 'Red Riding Hood,' 'The Lost Homeland' and 'Homeopathic *Tuberculinum*' contact that which cannot be said so well in any other way. We get alongside the experience and heighten our awareness of it in using metaphor.

Telling our stories in the present tense

In telling our stories in the present tense, allowing what we don't know as much as what we do to arise, we tell a new story, a surprising one. It *interrupts* the one we tell ourselves to keep ourselves stuck in our *comfort* (or indeed *discomfort*) stories.

Telling our stories anew reveals the state to an *active listener.*

This is vital practice. Vital in that it gets to the heart of the matter and vital in that the heart of the matter is always expressed in energetic ways; in metaphor, in body language, in 'aha' moments that cause us to move.

Have a go at actively listening to one of your stories.

Tell a story about yourself that you know very well. Tell it in the present tense. Write it down without pause, just as it comes, and in the present tense.

Now, go back over it. Pause and highlight any significant words and phrases, those that seem significant to you as you read. Don't think too much about it.

Write down the words and phrases.

Ask of each one, "What is this?"

In this story for example, "Throw cigarettes out the window" is waste. "What is wasting?" etc.

Track the story down using "What is?"

When you have tracked down each significant word and phrase as far as you can, write the story down again.

How is it changed? What have you learned that is new to you? How does this new story impact on you?

(See to Active Listening in Chapter Two, 'Let's Go Fly a Kite.')

The homeopath doesn't do very much in receiving the patient's story and just enough. Stories are given and received. Both sides of the relationship need to be present for stories to tell themselves. She accepts the tale. She asks about now.

"What is wasting?" she asks.

Not why? Or who? Or when? But that question which focuses and clarifies

"What is?"

It unravels the patient. She is undone. Her stories fall apart.

If it was 'there and then' but it isn't 'here and now,' as present pain and suffering, why bother remedying it? It is an old story, a story we tell ourselves to make sense of now.

What is the matter now ?

What stories do you tell to make sense of your life?

What causes do you attribute to the way things are now?

And what happens to those stories if you write one down? Really believe it. Really blame it for causing something of the way you are now?

Write it down in the present tense as if it is happening now.

Now look at it. Is it true? What is happening as you repeat this story with complete conviction? Does it stay the same or change? Maybe it's true and writing it down emphasises that. Maybe it's not all true. Maybe it isn't true at all. Maybe it's just a story. (Byron Katie 2002)

We Meet as People — Receiving and Taking the 'Case'

We meet as people. We take our places; one as therapist, practitioner or supervisor, the other as client, patient or supervisee. We make the 'case' together. This is the art-work we create in our relationship; the outcome of story, maps and models, art and craft. It is 'what the matter is' according to our healing modality. It is one thing for an Allopath: 'Rheumatism' is the matter. It is another for the homeopath: '*Tuberculinum* 1M' is the matter.

In 'receiving' another we are accepting what comes. We are open, soft, receptive, feminine. We are forgetting who we are and what we want. In 'taking' from another we are looking for something. We have something in mind. We are focussed, hard eyed, hunting, masculine. We are remembering who we are and what we want.

Both postures are needed to find out what the matter is. When we receive we may give our full attention to the other. We may end up quite stuck in empathy if we aren't also able to be aware of ourselves and our observations as we listen. (See Chapter Three, 'Cheetah,' Fusing Is Normal.)

When we 'take' the story, we are listening in order to find something we think we need in order to make sense of it. We may be literally taking the other's story from them and making it our own and unrecognisable to them if we aren't careful. This is what happens when the *case* we have made for a person does not fit them so well. (See Chapter Six, 'And the Boat Capsized in Deep Water.')

There is no more virtue in receiving over taking as such. What is required now, moment to moment? That is the question.

What happens when you sit back and receive, soft eyed, all that comes to you?

What happens when you sit forward and go hunting for what is there, with a hard eyed looking?

What happens to you? To who or what you are looking at? To what you get? To what you give? What do you give in each case?

What is the quality of each?

What feelings are associated with each?

These are questions in the spirit of inquiring into the nature of our presence and its effects.

Embodiment

A fellow practitioner puts her experience of 'presence' like this —

> "It is also possible to sit in the interface between being with ourself and being with the other. The key to this is embodiment. Using awareness of our own body we are able to be 'with' ourself while also open to the other. One way to do this is to soften our gaze and become aware of the space between the other and ourselves. This can bring us into a deeper contact with our body and open up our awareness of the space around to include our patient. It also tends to bring us back in contact with our breath, thus we begin to drop into our body, relax and open to the other from a grounded place. In being embodied, sitting clearly in our own space, we open up the space for the other to be and for us to simply receive them." (Anna Murray-Preece, 2004)

Also see to the developmental paradigm of embodiment, projection and role (E.P.R.) (Jennings, 1994)

We describe ourselves as '*burnt* or *burning-out*' when we are out of touch with our own *embodied* experience. We can only trot out our comfort stories; there is no spark of life in them or in us really. Some very successful practices run on burn out as there is a cosy reassurance in sharing comfort stories and no threat or promise of real change. We may be disembodied in another way: Practice may be characterised by a feeling we can go on forever without tiring. We are inspired and insightful. We know what the matter is before the other has barely sat down with us. We have left our selves completely and collapse must surely follow in one way or another!'

Comfort story: Elemental story

This chapter focuses on stories told in words; actively listening to the spaces in between, to the elemental story conveyed by the words, to their simple meaning. Homeopathy is a narrative therapy. We work expressly with words.

Our task is to go deeper into our *comfort* stories to reach our basic drives; our attachments and fears; to hear the *elemental* story. (See Chapter Seven, 'The Dog's Story.')

In staying with the experience, telling it in the present tense, believing every word, pausing to ask *"What is this?"* we are actively listening and tracking down to the elemental story.

We know when we have arrived because physical changes happen. We may get excited, more alert, sit up, wake up, look shocked or surprised, get interested, feel fearful or anxious. All this will register physically. We are engaged in the experience now. Both listener and teller know it. We are onto something. Follow the thread. Track the story down to its elements. Here we are connected to the bigger stories of myth and archetype. Here we are connected to the natural world of animals, plants and minerals, to the heavens above and to the seas below.

In being present; really in our bodies, in the moment, we register the changes. We sense, feel, intuit and think them. We are guided where to go next. The story tells us. We don't think up the next question. It comes down. The words are already there. Track them. Follow. Don't interpret or worry. Stay with it.

The elemental story always contains a surprise; a connection not made before, an awakening, a serendipitous happening. Comfort stories are characterised by their familiarity, their rightness, their neatness, their definite sense of right and wrong and positive causation. They may be very uncomfortable stories, but they are nonetheless familiar and there is some comfort in that.

Elemental story connects to movement and to motivation— to what really gets us up out of bed each morning and to the manner in which we do that. We could say it is about what 'drives' us and what that drive looks like.

How am I moving? What are the qualities of it? Is it the graceful motion of the gazelle, the lumber of an elephant, the imperceptible movements of a continental drift, a willow in the breeze, the immobility of a rock?

In the patient's story in this chapter, she is moving this way and that, restlessly and with frustration— as if she is banging her head on the wall. It is at this level of movement and stripped down description that we find the story that counts; the vital one.

Vital practice acquires a nose for comfort stories and goes on sniffing at the flaw, the crack, the incongruity in the tale, until the thing falls apart and remakes itself in quite another way.

> "There is a crack, a crack in everything. It's where the light gets in." (Cohen, 1992)

Whatever the healing modality, inquiring into the story is vital practice. The inquiry may be with the hands rather than in the telling and it is the same process: What is happening and how is it moving? From where to where and in what manner?

In every case, differentiating between comfort story and elemental story decides whether it is palliation we are intending, or *cure*. There being a time and place for both, it is as well to know what we are about and what it is we communicate wittingly or not about what it is we are doing.

Stories are co-created. We are social animals us human beings. So aware of the stories we bring to the therapeutic relationship is a vital practice. We each bring expectations for sure. These may be met, changed or developed in the course of the relationship. We bring maps, models, theories, and treatment plans and they become a part of what we are listening to and the story we make together. (see C.E.P —Competence, Expectation and Process model in 'Vital Kit, Making Working Relationship.')

This movement between being with the other and being with ourselves Buber called 'inclusion.' (M. Buber, 1996 edition) As a way of practising and supervising ourselves, inclusion allows the elemental story; the vital story, to emerge from the movement between actively listening to the other, paying attention to our own maps, models, and ideas and to our senses, intuitions and felt-senses. No wonder we miss so much of the action at the time! And what a wonder it is too when we do meet each other in what Buber called an '*I-Thou*' moment, that moment of healing when there are no longer two in the relationship. It is as if we are as one; united in a moment of bliss before we inevitably separate again.

The skill needed in order to be present to the moment is active listening.

Actively Listening

Actively listening to ourselves as we listen to another — with our ears, eyes, hearts and minds open. Simple yes? Easy yes?

Try it. I intend to every time my 11 year old is playing on his games player and I want him to move on to something else. I try to listen to what is bothering me and to listen to what he is telling me about what his character is doing in the story he is making. I haven't heard us yet.

Here are some daily practices encouraging active listening:

Being present:

Sitting comfortably and quietly without disturbance (phone turned off) and with enough time: Turn your attention to your breath. (See relaxation exercise in 'Introduction, How Do You Listen to Yourself?' page 7.)

Now watch and listen to your thoughts, senses, feelings, worries come and go by turn. Watch them come and let them go, as if you are watching them on a screen before you or listening to them on the radio. If you are getting stuck in one and it is thinking or worrying you, return your attention to the breath. You are not your thoughts, neither are you your worries.

Empathetic listening:

Again sitting quietly and undisturbed: Bring to mind a story told by another that you have found difficult to hear or have not yet made time to hear. Perhaps you feel you have heard it all before. Perhaps you feel you know how it will end. Perhaps you are frightened of what you might hear. Let yourself listen to it afresh. Just listen. No need to respond. No need to do anything at all. Tell yourself the story in their words. Notice your own interventions as they arise and return to telling the story in their words, time and manner. What do you hear?

Silent listening:

Bring to your awareness some minor concern, worry or problem. (Don't start with a huge obstacle.)

Now, stay with it. Let it come to you. Stay with it. Do nothing. Don't try to fix it. Don't try to change it. Stay with the experience of it. Feel it. Think it. Imagine it. Sense it. What is it like? Be still with it. Let it come.

Is it still a problem? What is it now?

Reflective listening:

Tell yourself something you say very often, like "I'm fed up" or "I'd like a change" or "I wish." What do you mean when you say that? Stay with it. What is "fed up," "change" or "wishing"?

Inclusiveness:

That story I couldn't empathise with that I have now practiced empathising with (above), can I move back and forth now between how it is for me and how it is for them? Am I attached to either place? What is it like to see it from here and from there?

Listening with a partner:

Take a partner and offer to listen to them for 5 or 10 minutes. Ask them how they would like to be listened to: In silence just to be heard?

> With responses from you that might enable them to hear themselves better; that is reflective listening?
>
> Empathetically and with a summary or metaphor from you at the end to share what you have heard?
>
> Have a go.
>
> Swap places and be listened to in the way you want.
>
> What do you learn about how you listen and what you listen to?
>
> And about how you like to be listened to?

In actively listening, embodying our own experience, we *get alongside* the experience of another. We connect with the story, and in so doing, we come to realise that story telling is of itself a healing art.

Interrupting the Story

In accepting a story, really listening to it, it changes before our eyes. Stories are magic. We start by telling a story we know and end up with the story telling us!

Supervision is that way of looking at and listening to the story that quite simply *interrupts* the *comfort story* taking us down further into a deeper connectedness with it in simply listening without wanting it to be different.

According to this definition we supervise ourselves and are supervised moment to moment anyway, whether we do supervision or not in any formal way as a part of our training or practice.

We can practice any healing modality in a more or less supervisory way. The more attached we are to our own stories about how it is and the less connected we are to our own embodied experience, the less supervisory we are being.

(And that goes for writing this book— it is very hard to practice what you preach.) The more experienced we are the more we become settled into our comfortable ways of practicing. It is then we need to *"wake up to the dream"* of practice (Balint, 1959), in being more not less, supervisory of ourselves.

Relationship

To *interrupt* practice or to *wake up* to it we establish a 'working relationship' with ourselves and with those we invite to help inquire within. This is a relationship that is able and willing to work with the level of distrust there must be if we are to take any risks at all. (See 'Vital Kit, Working Relationship.')

It is in healing relationship that the dis-ease is revealed to the *active listener*. If we knew what the matter was we would no doubt fix it ourselves. We need each other in order to re-create the matter in a safe enough, risky enough, supervisory enough relationship.

Brian Kaplin (2001) calls the art of case taking a 'homeopathic conversation.' It captures perfectly the sense of relationship between practitioner and client. His own journey as a doctor of medicine, meeting pathology in post mortem, to homeopath, meeting people in all manner of health and disease, is most vividly and joyously narrated.

Healing and Shape Shifting

Matter refers to substance without form. When we ask *"What is the matter?"* We are asking *"What form are you in?"* *"What shape are you in?"* *"What are you like?"* *"What is the metaphor for the shape you are in?"* (See Chapter Four, 'Ain't Gonna Die for You.')

It is 'vital practice' to *get alongside* another as the homeopath gets alongside this patient. It is *being* homeopathic, not just 'doing' homeopathy, to do as she does; to make minimum interventions in order to clarify the unique patterning; the shape of this young woman.

It is itself shape shifting to be actively listened to. The story shifts, the world tilts and we change shape along with it.

We talk about *'the shape I'm in'* or *'being in bad shape.'* At this basic level, dis-easing and healing is about shape shifting. We are *'out of shape'* and when we recover we are *'back in shape.'* Healing is shamanic.

The remedy as story, as shape, as movement, meets an apparently completely different entity — a person is well met by the *potentised* disease product of a cow! (*Tuberculinum Bovinum*)

In taking stories seriously enough to inquire carefully into them, so that we see the patterns, the shapes, the movements we are making, we are sharing in a privileged moment of revelation; one that is no less life changing for the listener as it is for the story teller — as we see in the next story.

LET'S GO
FLY A KITE

A Practitioner's Story

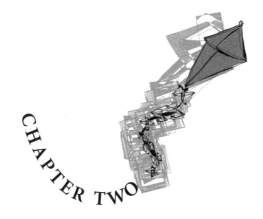

CHAPTER TWO

"If you've never flown a big kite you won't know what I mean but when you put one up in the air on a windy day you are hanging onto the ground because it is trying to pick you up and throw you forty foot down the beach. There's a feeling of scared, exhilarated, I'm not sure what's going to happen next. When you realise that you can get away with it just by pulling lines and moving your arms, it's like dancing. You've got to dance in the wind with it, just dance, and use your whole body. You don't just use your arms and hands but your head to toe and when they get the feel of that (with the big ones you are holding onto them and dancing with them), it's just the daft looks on their faces. They're picking something up from nature. Is the wind in your ear? Or on your face? Or hitting you on the back of your head? If it is on the back of your head, it's in the right place. Listen to your body. Feel your body. Where's it cold? Where's it windy? And if you turn round a little bit, now where is the wind? There is just this look."

Peter works with adults with profound learning difficulties in residential care. He takes them kite buggying. It *interrupts* their daily routine. It interrupts his too.

The people Peter cares for have very little say in their lives. He takes them to the beach on a windy day and holds them while they try to fly a fidgety kite in strong weather. They don't stay in the classroom and talk about their feelings of helplessness; they haven't that habit anyway. Peter shirks the classroom whenever he can. He comes alive in the elements. He works with this aspect of himself with his clients. They go out, take risks, shock themselves a little, do it in 3D; themselves, the kite and the wind. In this way they are getting both the experience of powerlessness and the effort to take control.

"If you take anyone's life that lives in that group, they live with the same people, who they don't necessarily like. And for anything up to ten years, with people they are not that keen on, even scared of, or just indifferent to. They have no control over their food. In theory they have, they are supposed to pick the shopping list. In reality it doesn't happen. They have no control over where they go everyday. They go to the day centre from 10 to 4 they come back to the house they have tea blah blah blah, club on a Wednesday night and possibly a pub over the weekend. That's their life. Stick something that would be very small, that to us would be very small, that's different…

Hardly anything at all needs to be said. The experience is so new and so overwhelming. A man who never speaks to anyone, never thinks to share anything in his life or of his life, or of anyone else's, except to meet his basic needs, turns to someone and says

"That was great, you should have a go."

Presence

I travel along the coast road from my home along the high seventeen miles above Chesil Bank, past St Catherine's Chapel on Abbotsbury Hill to Bridport and on, up into the Honiton Hills, all the way to the School of Homeopathy in Uffculme in Devon. I travel this way maybe twice a month. I know the way.

I know the way home too. It is a different way. It is now all back to front. It may as well be other hills, another beach, a different saint to pray a different prayer to. I don't always recognise it as the same route.

I don't remember because I wasn't there in the first place. *'I am on my way to school'* and then *'I am on my way home.'* Two different journeys. If however I am really paying attention to my driving; noticing the way as I pass, the hedgerows and flowers, the trees and road signs; really paying attention, then the journey there and back starts to connect as the same road. I am not just *'going to the School'* or *'going home'* my mind in anticipation; I am here, on the road. I am present and I remember.

When we are alive to what is happening now, we wake up to *what is* instead of falling asleep in the *comfort stories* of our clinical routines and daily practices. (See Chapter One, 'What is the Matter?') Not to stretch a point, we all have profound learning difficulties when it comes to being present to our own, moment to moment experience. (Bion, 1961; Stern, 2004)

Practice happens and it is gone. It can be difficult to stay with at the time and even harder to reflect on what happened afterwards unless we are pulled up short by something; a so called *critical incident,* something that disturbs or awakes our interest. Only something very small needs to be noticed to wake us up.

Re-membering

The purpose of doing supervision is to re-member practice; to put it together in another way. It does this by *'perturbing the stuck narratives.'* (H.R. Maturana & F. Varela, 1984 in Tselikas-Portman, 1999)

The supervisory voice acts as an *'irritator'* interrupting repetitive stories and facilitating the construction of new ones. As a result, practice is 're-membered,' literally 'dis-membered' and then put back together again so that it moves more easily.

Another way of putting this is to say that questions brought to supervision are not so much answered as 're-framed' so that the questioner can answer them for herself.

Recording

Recording ourselves in practice and supervision, on audio or video, helps us remember what happened. It is a fast route to shattering illusions of what we think we do in practice. Recording has been reviewed in an educational context by Kagan among others and called 'Interpersonal Process Recall' (IPR). (N. Kagan, 1980)

With permission, record a supervision or practice session in order to look and listen to it. (So as to minimise the artificiality of the situation, it is best to record all of the sessions with someone rather than to start half way through the relationship or to stop and start recording.)

Now, listen to the recording either with a supervisor or by yourself. Look and listen to your interventions. (Any intervention from you, not necessarily a wordy one.) Here are some questions you might ask of your self:

Who was this intervention for? *

What happened next?

What was I intending to do in making it?

What did I want to say or do instead?

What would have happened if I had said or done that?

What would the risk have been in doing that?

How was I perceived?

How did I want to be perceived?

What was the 'felt –sense'?

Take just five-minute sections of the recording and ask these questions. Ask your supervisor, yourself or peer supervising group to listen and make observations.

What do you think you do in practice? What do you do in this excerpt?

(Carroll, 1996, p. 130 and * a most useful intervention by Carroll in a one-to-one supervision session.)

I record some of my sessions as a supervisor. I like to think that my interventions tend towards minimal, empathetic and edgy. In fact my voice on tape often has too much of authority in it feel. I am intending to 'get alongside' the supervisee, yet in the end the supervisee seems too often to be following me. Ouch. I am often mortified by what I hear on my tapes. And I am instructed.

Peter records the conversation with me about taking the residents of a care home on a kite buggying outing. In telling the story, getting into the feeling of doing the kite flying, he sees what a profoundly transforming event it can be. He can't simply dismiss it and himself as 'shirking' the daily routine. He tells the ordinary tale in the present tense to capture the moment, communicating a powerful shift. (See Chapter One, 'What is the Matter?')

The telling turns the event into an experience he can evaluate. This is vital practice for Peter as much as for the previously silent man flying the kite. Peter can have renewed confidence in 'shirking' the classroom in favour of days out in the knowledge that he is working well while having fun. (See Chapter Five, 'Magic Glasses.')

Healing Relationship — Homeopathic Relationship

The quality of the relationship in which we remember is going to affect what we learn from the experience. Are we going to be interested in what we learn or excruciated by it and want to forget about it as soon as possible? (See to 'Shame On You' below.)

A homeopathic approach to relationship is to begin by *getting alongside* as Peter literally gets alongside the kite flyers. He holds them while they take their risks.

But what difference does it make how we do it so long as we find out what we are stuck in and shift it? Why do it homeopathically?

When I experiment with going for change, *before* I have gotten alongside, guess what? They don't go. (Ask any teenager or parent of teenagers and they will tell every gruesome story known to man of what happens when we go up against resistance…)

Boundaries — now that is something else. Working in formal space, creating a boundary for the relationship, serves to heighten awareness of and respect for what happens. I may get down and play tug o war with my puppy— but I have to stand up again and take the toy away from her every time — if I don't want a sharp nip from her the next time we play.

Getting Alongside

Getting alongside, practicing *like cures like* in our relationships (as well as in choosing the curative remedy in a homeopathic practice), involves us in being more interested in what is happening now, more willing to learn from that than we are in putting across our own story.

In getting alongside another, mercifully we forget ourselves. We *get alongside* in many ways, shapes and forms; in our body language, our posture and demeanour, the quality of our attention, the openness of our hearts to new experience and to a fellow sufferer. It is not necessarily a wordy business.

In fact wordy interventions are possibly the lowest potency responses. Do you feel your focus on this drifting yet? They lack the direction and power of body language and metaphor. Metaphor, poetry and images in few words tend to be more potent than long narratives. Peter knows this in taking the adults in his care out of the classroom and into a dramatic sensory experience. 'Doing it' means we get it in one. (See Chapter Three, 'Cheetah' and Chapter Four, 'Ain't Gonna Die for You.')

Empty Relationship and Echo

The supervisory relationship is an *empty* relationship in that it is set up to *parallel* or *echo* the practice in order to inquire into it. If we fill it up with *cases* we are 'stuck' with then it doesn't have room to be itself and to find in itself the dynamics of the matter. We bring ourselves to supervision; whether we are the supervisor or the supervisee. This is where we begin. We introduce others to the relationship; clients, children, students or whoever; each seen through our eyes or acted out through ourselves. Supervision is an empty relationship we fill with shadows. (The exception is 'live' supervision where client, practitioner and supervisor are in the room — along with their shadows (see "Vital Kit, Contexts' Guides for Live Supervision).

Anything that is not yet out in the open in the practice inevitably gets acted out in the supervision. Whatever can't be seen clearly or owned up to at the time, is brought *'raw'* to the session where it is *'cooked'* in the process. (Shipton, ed., 1997)

Paying attention to what is happening, in the 'here and now' of the supervision is a way of remembering what happened in the 'there and then' of practice because the supervision will parallel the practice.

> "Margory Doehrman (1976) has done one of the very few pieces of research on paralleling that exist, in which she studied both the therapy sessions and the supervision on the therapy of 12 different people. In the introduction to Doehrman's study, Mayman writes: 'What is strongly suggested by Doehrman's study, a result that she herself admits took her by surprise, was the fact that powerful parallel processes were present in every

patient-therapist-supervisor relationship she studied." (Doehrman, 1976:4 in Hawkins & Shohet, 2000, p. 82)

It is the task of the supervision to work with this *echo* or *parallel process* to reveal what the matter is. It is also the case that the supervisory relationship will parallel back to the therapeutic one (also noted by Doehrman): What happens in the supervision finds echo in practice. It is a cycle: Patient tells a story in practice which is then told in supervision and retold in practice and round again. Each time round the cycle and it becomes clearer, more elemental, both more characteristic and more universal.

That is if we listen actively to what it is. We are bringing our own prejudices to it in the way of maps, models, ideas and old stories. We bring these often without any awareness of what it is we are doing and then the cycle may be more like playing 'Whispers'; one story is brought but quite another emerges…

This is the experience of many of us as we start out in practice. We have a good story in one hand that the client shows and tells. We have a different one in the other, the one we have constructed as a remedy response or treatment plan. Both are very good stories in their own right, and the one has very little to do with the other, for in the process of analysing and constructing a response we have lost the original story.

How do we *wake up* to the *elemental story* instead of playing 'Whispers'?

When we pay attention to what is happening in the supervision the noticing is that the story will act out here. Like those books we have as children where there is an image hidden in the main illustration:

"Find the treasure chest hidden in the picture of children playing on a beach."

We are distracted by the story shown in the main picture. We look and look and can't see the treasure chest drawn into the tumble of picnic food spilling from the basket. We are looking hungrily at the delicious picnic. Then, as we soften our gaze and let the picture come to us, we see it. Sometimes, we screw up our eyes and 'hard eye' the picture and then we spot it.

Listening to the 'echo' in the context of a process model reminds us there are many aspects to relationship. (Hawkins and Shohet, 2000, Ch. 6) Not everyone focuses on what happens in the supervision to parallel what happens in practice. Perfectly useful supervision happens without it. The suggestion is that by paying attention to the 'echo', since it happens anyway, we gain knowledge of the more shadowy, Dionysian aspects of the relationship under review. Hawkins and Shohet developed the Seven Level model of supervision in response to noticing that different supervision relationships adopt different styles and foci and can result in different outcomes. In drawing up their model of possible processes they extend the possible field being over-viewed. They identify …

> "at least four elements
>
> - A supervisor
>
> - A therapist
>
> - A client
>
> - A work context
>
> Of these four, normally only the supervisor and the therapist are directly present in the supervision session, except in live supervision. However, the client and the work context are carried into the session in both the conscious awareness and the unconscious sensing of the therapist…" (Hawkins and Shohet, 2000, pp. 68–69)

This gives the seven areas to focus on for clues about what is energising, driving or moving the relationship at this point.

In summary these are

1. The content of the supervisory session.

2. The therapeutic response — strategies and interventions.

3. The therapeutic relationship.

4. The practitioner's process.

5. The supervisory relationship.

6. The supervisor's process

7. Focus on the wider context.

In focusing on the three aspects of the supervisory relationship (4 to 6) in the supervision itself we make space to notice the 'echo' of the original story—the elements we couldn't hear at the time and that may well be the clue to what the matter is. (Hawkins and Shohet, 2000, Ch. 6)

What follows is a practical exercise to try in a group supervision to demonstrate and inquire into this 'echo' phenomenon. It can be fascinating to see it happen and this can mean we stay in the thrall of it rather than move on to see what light the 'echo' can shed on what is happening. This is why in this particular exercise it is important to give the original supervisee the last word, having first listened to all the observations, so that she can assess the usefulness of the exercise in helping her to respond to the issues she has brought to supervision.

In the same spirit, the facilitator role is important in holding each person to their role and task so that the *case* is brought forward to be clarified each time rather than speculated upon and interpreted at whim. The facilitator or group supervisor holds the story or stories as they unfold, providing a *meta* commentary that takes account of the different kinds of sense making provoked by the unfolding story. These are tentatively offered. The facilitator attempts to notice when she herself is becoming a part of the echo — digging in to find her internal observer. The reality is, she goes in and out of consciousness of the story — now a part of it, now the story teller. (See Chapter Four, 'Ain't Gonna Die for You.' Facilitator as Story teller)

Echo.

Two chairs are placed; one for a supervisee and the other for a supervisor. A group participant volunteers to be supervisee and brings something to supervision for ten minutes or so. Another group member elects to supervise her. The rest of the group sits around the room and practices observing the interaction. (see 'Vital Kit, Contexts': Live Clinical Group Supervision — the role of observer.) The group facilitator or an elected recorder makes notes or video records the action. (see 'Vital Kit, Contexts': Recording the Action.)

At the end of the first ten minute supervision session, the supervisee rejoins the group. The supervisor then takes the chair vacated by the supervisee. Another group member sits in the supervisor's chair and supervises the previous supervisor on her session. The supervisory pair may be focusing on any aspect of the session, using for example, the Hawkins and Shohet model. This continues, with each supervisee returning to the group and a new supervisor coming to supervise the last one on their session. The number of sessions vary. The run may naturally come to an end with a catharsis or a natural sense of ending or else by running out of steam or time. After this, the group give short feedback on what they have observed. (see Feedback & CORBS in 'Vital Kit, Guides for Triading.')

The elected facilitator then refers to the recording to bring together the sense of the action. The original supervisee has the last word in giving feedback on what the run of supervision sessions have revealed to her.

Every time I have practiced this piece of *art-play*, the elemental story has been echoed through the sessions. Each session brings out another nuance. At the close the 'case' is clarified, *re-framed* or resolved.

For the residents of the care home, kite flying 'echos' the sense of being small and unable and the enormous effort it takes to get back any control. They literally embody the experience. Often on medication and under exercised, lethargy becomes the comfort state. Fighting a kite on a windy beach literally wakes them up!

Safe Enough — Risky Enough

It is the task of the supervision to hold the practitioner, as Peter holds the kite flyer. Supervision does need to be a safe enough place for us to explore and to play, to grow and develop in skills and confidence. This mirrors the safe enough relationship between practitioner and client and the *"good enough"* relationship between parent and child. (Bettleheim, 1976)

If there is no risk, no interruption of the *comfort story*, then nothing happens. This is what I call a *'tea and sympathy'* practice:

Oh I know, it's terrible/difficult/heart sinking isn't it?

This is encouraging an *'us* and *them'* division and a nice victim — persecutor split. (See Chapter Four, 'Ain't Gonna Die for You.')

Peter is often surprised by the outcomes of sessions with people with learning difficulties. He may set something up with the expectation of achieving one thing; physical challenge for example with the kite flying, and get instead a remarkable social breakthrough. People not ordinarily given to conversation for the joy of it suddenly get interested in sharing experience. Peter shifts the notion of himself as a classroom shirker, seeing his strengths as a helper who is prepared to *'have a go.'*

In inquiring into our practice, we pay attention to the voices we invite to inquire with us. We might ask

"Are they safe enough voices, not unduly harsh or critical? Not too fearful and timid for exploration? Can they hold the process of inquiry?"

This refers to the voices within us, our internal critic or comfort voice, as much as to those people we choose to work with. (See Voices in 'Vital Kit, Guides for Triading' and Contracting in 'Vital Kit, Working Relationship.')

Shame On You

A lot of us will have been brought up with not just negative voices, but shame based learning.

"Oh how could you have done that? "

"You are awful."

"Shame on you!"

(Not even what you have done is awful but you yourself.) You know the sort of stuff. When I say I am mortified in re-running a tape of my practice (above), there is some squirm and some embarrassment, there is also some interest in noticing that my fantasy and the reality are different. I want to learn more how it is. I have enough conviction, most of the time, that it is practice and not perfect.

We cannot always experience being known as a benign event, even if the explicit intention is to be helpful.

Shame is in the room and so the most innocuous remark can be badly received. There is so much opportunity to experience shame in supervision; the shame of not knowing; of being found out; found wanting; of not being good enough / wise enough / clever enough / loving enough.

Supervision can be seen as a chance to re-create shame in order to heal it. 'Shame' and 'shaman' share the same root — we are 'out of shape' when we are ashamed. Healing relationship, including supervision, is shape shifting. (Hewson, 1999)

In practice when shame strikes us and we don't know what to do or how to be, this is the moment that really tests us in staying with *what is*. How can we get interested at this point? How to see shame as another story and just hear it without being a part of it? When we identify with it we are ashamed. The remembering is, I am not my shame.

Art-play

Peter plays with the adults in his care. It seems to wake people in the sleep of institutional and chemically sedated lives. The art of flying a kite may seem to have little to do on the face of it with social skills, yet it makes a connection with motive force, with something so powerful it must be communicated, most unusually, to others as *"Have a go!"* (See Chapter Five, 'Magic Glasses.')

Art-play wakes us up.

Telling a story in the present tense, as if it is happening now, is one way to connect with its vital nature. Tracking it through *comfort stories* to feelings, sensation and physical movement until we find the hidden treasure recognised instantly between us as a moment of catharsis.

Showing practice as a picture, or illustrating it on a map is another way to *wake up* to it. (See Introduction and Chapter Three, 'Cheetah.')

In changing the modality, new and more elemental images arise.

Acting the practice out by ourselves, or with the help of peers in a *triad* ('Vital Kit, Guides for Triading') or group brings it to life in that we are doing it rather than trying to recreate the experience in words alone. We invite our senses, our actions, our whole selves to experience the state, the stuck response or the relationship between us.

I am calling this energetic or vital practice for the purposes of inquiry *art-play*. It may simply take the form of adopting the posture of the other; sitting and holding yourself as she does. It may mean getting up and walking as she does, talking as she does, making gestures as she does. It may mean making the grimaces and frowns, the looks she makes.

Whenever we invoke inquiry into an absent person it is a good idea to bring them in with respect.

"I am bringing my relationship with Fred to supervision. I am finding it hard to respond to him. This empty chair represents Fred in our inquiry. Come and sit down Fred."

OK so a bit cheesy — but compare it to:

"I'm bringing a 'stuck case.' A man of 32 diagnosed with chronic rhinitis. He doesn't respond to anything I do."

Whose problem is this?

Empty Chairs:

The empty chair is placed in a supervision where the client is not actually present. (see 'Vital Kit, Contexts' Live Supervision Clinical Group) as we invite the presence of the relationship under review.

Working alone, you can put an empty chair out and use it to move in and out of the experience of different people in the story. Go and sit on it as the other and tell the story from there and then move back to your chair and respond.

Working with a peer you can take the place of the other and ask the peer to be the practitioner. Now give the story of the other person as if it is your own. Literally sitting in their place. This promotes empathy if you are stuck in your own story about the other person. Your peer can 'model' for you another response to the one you are stuck in.

With three you can ask another peer to observe the interaction and tell you after the story telling and active listening what it is she has noticed. (We are normally so engaged in the story that an observer, paying attention to the 'here and now,' can perceive elements not normally available to us. See 'Vital Kit, Guides for Triading' Role of Observer.)

You can allocate a person to be 'shadow' voice to the presenter or receiver; one not clearly expressed but felt in some way. The 'shadow' is a loose cannon in the interaction; acting out and speaking up whatever she hears or feels, intuits or senses is not said. The shadow takes risks (see 'Vital Kit, Guides for Triading' Role of Shadow).

Play with the form. You can heighten a voice; focus on one voice, hear them all together.

(See 'Vital Kit, Guides for Triading' and to Chapter Three, 'Cheetah' and Chapter Four, 'Ain't Gonna Die for You.')

Art-play gives us a sense of the whole interaction; its quality, its essence; the way it moves; the direction and pace. Group supervisions make optimum spaces for art-play — the focus of the next two stories.

Practising our healing art can be like flying that big kite; becoming by turns the flyer, the kite, the beach, the high and windy day.

CHEETAH

Story Becomes a 'Case': There Are No Stuck Cases. Group Supervision Story 1

CHAPTER THREE

A *case* is the sense a practitioner makes of someone's original story. People come to see us. They become clients or patients. We take and receive their story. We weave a case from it according to our arts and respond to the sense we make of it. There are many acts of translation involved; many stories to be heard and retold; refined and revised in the quest for the more *elemental* one. (Ryan, 2002)

Story becomes a 'case'

A 'case' is what a practitioner works with. We bring 'stuck cases' to supervision but in order to find out what the matter is we need to find the people in the case — the person who comes as client, the person who comes as practitioner and the one who comes as supervisor. What are their stories?

As a participant in a group supervision, we were asked to focus on someone we were stuck with in practice. I brought to mind a woman bringing many distressing and changing symptoms. Her name is Helen.

Each time Helen comes to see me she brings new sufferings, sensations and dreams. She laughs while describing her inability to find either peace or contentment anywhere in the world. She feels ungrounded and disconnected. I am finding it hard in my turn both to stay with her and to keep my own ground.

I suspect my issues are a little fused with hers. How to 'get myself out of the way' so to speak, so that I can see her more clearly?

The group supervisor suggests we act out our situations to give the opportunity to get down to the senses and actions involved rather than rationalise, explain or tell ourselves our *comfort stories* about our cases; those explanations of what isn't working that we already know about.

I choose three companions from the group to help me with my drama. These could be three significant people at the beginning of Helen's life or they could be me, Helen and the case. I'm not sure yet. We begin by taking a few moments to pay attention to the breath. I am calling Helen to mind. I adopt Helen's posture. I crouch down a little and apart from the others. Spontaneously I ask the three to face me. Immediately I sense being in danger. I feel frustrated and pretty hopeless already.

I am feeling too that the exercise is trivial and pointless, since while it is enlarging and dramatising the situation, it is only reaffirming my stuckness. I know she is frightened. My problem is that as a homeopath I can't quite see how she is moving with this.

The group facilitator suggests I stay with the drama and see what happens. I pull first one, then another of the companions over to my side to stand next to me. We are now all facing one. I am looking to him and then behind me. A vague image is forming. I am at the edge of a cliff. I must leap or turn and fight. I realise this is absolute terror. Who or what am I?

I am crouching now ready to spring.

Nameless and formless, I begin to take shape. I am a lone mother cheetah protecting my cubs. I draw them closer. I am being threatened by a rogue male, coming to kill the cubs. He is trying to scare me off. I find my voice. I don't run or jump and I don't fight. I can't win in a fight and I can't run or jump off and leave the cubs. I open my mouth and I roar. (Do cheetahs roar?) I stand my ground. I make such an alarming and unexpectedly fierce sound that I frighten the attacker off!

The 'actors' are following my cues in attempting to give me the performances I need for this dramatic recreation. (It helps if you are willing to get it wrong and be the fool, suffer confusion and lose track of what you are doing and why — a leap of faith!)

This dramatic recreation of a stuck situation puts me in touch with an *elemental story:* There is only a choice between running or fighting. I discover in the *art-play,* the *dramatic re-creation,* the third option — standing ground. This is communicated to me *dramatically.* I get it in one: I have been fusing with the patient's 'fight or flight' dilemma. The dramatic art-play restores me to my own ground.

(I realise, in remembering this story, that writing this book is another *echo* of the same tale. Standing ground in the sense of speaking your own truth can be a scary thing. I have wrestled this project to the ground to get it down on paper.)

The only intervention the group supervisor makes is to ask me to stay with the process when I am feeling stuck and downhearted during the *homeopathic aggravation* of my 'stuckness' — feeling more hopeless and frustrated.

In homeopathic terms: She is making a *minimum intervention.* The wild animal drama *potentises* or energises my dilemma. The cheetah story is analogous to my situation. *Like cures like.* It corresponds to it.

The shift comes in the drama. I can reflect on its specific relevance to the patient once I have made that shift and am freer to think. The point is, energetically the shift is made; I am released from the 'fight or flight' dilemma.

It isn't a simple matter of Helen being in a wild cat state. The remedy that emerges from differentiating remedy responses to the 'fight or flight' situation is another one with acute awareness of danger; *Hydrogen.* (Sherr, 1991)

The *Hydrogen* story is one of spacing out, a feeling of separation from the world and the body. I experienced Helen's symptoms as disconnected. It is a cold remedy, dreaming of death. Helen feels disconnected from the world as if she could just let go into death. This does not trouble her, rather her concern at this point is for spiritual enlightenment.

At the time of bringing Helen to this group supervision I was finding it difficult to stay alongside her as she resisted earthly life. She took flight in a flurry of distracting symptoms and life crises. It was hard for us both to stay with it.

In dramatising the situation in the group supervision, the conflict comes sharply into focus. In naming it for myself, through experiencing a shadow of it, I was then able to stay with the patient, as she painfully and most cautiously, with much fighting and flighting, came into her own life.

With the remedy *Hydrogen* 10M, she was able to 'come to earth' so to speak and eventually make and maintain relationship with much less pain and suffering. Hydrogen can almost never be encountered on earth in its free state. (Vermeulen 1996)

I didn't know of the *Cheetah* clinical proving at the time of this case. (Sankaran, 2003) Here is a thumbnail sketch of the male cheetah from notes taken at that seminar:

> The cheetah. does not need water. The cheetah chases prey down with a swipe to the leg to fell it. The cheetah runs the fastest. The theme is survival of the strong and the fast. He is a single hunter, the victim and aggressor.

And additional information about the female:

> The female and her cubs are also prey to the male. He goes around in a pack of males. He takes no part in caring for her or the young. He may well kill them. She needs to protect herself and her young from him. She has to hunt as well as to nurture in order to feed her young. He is not her mate but her predator.

This story of the female cheetah reflects Helen's history with remarkable clarity. It heightens the terror aspect as the impulse for separating: She describes her life as a series of flights from threatening situations — she is literally 'frightened out of her life.' She doesn't however fight back with a swipe or a roar. Her movement is to detach, isolate and expand into universal consciousness (*Hydrogen*).

There Are No Stuck Cases

We bring *stuckness* to supervision; a stuck case or difficult patient, and in the course of observing what is actually happening we find it is in some way our own stuckness and within our own power to shift.

There are of course plainly difficult cases, requiring skill and ingenuity from the practitioner. The task of the supervision here is to clarify the issues and bring clinical wisdom in the light of greater experience to the matter. These difficult cases are not necessarily stuck however.

'Stuckness' is always our affair; brought about by being attached to particular feelings, ideas or outcomes. Helen is who she is and what she is. When we are able to perceive and accept what truly is, the healing response arises of itself. Easy said of course. Developing curiosity over judgement, attachment and shame truly is a daily practice!

A healing artist does not interpret or work harder than the other; *"Be more lazy and stupid than the patient"* is how Sankaran puts it. Let them tell you what the matter is. Track them in staying with their story and finding out what it is and what it means. And then come back to yourself.

Fusing Is Normal

In staying with what is happening, in following others, we will take on or *fuse* with someone at some point. This is normal. It is to be welcomed even. A homeopathic *proving* is a *fusing* of ourselves with the elemental nature of the potentised substance. We need the myriad of experiencing. We realise in this way that there is no 'us' and 'them' but only facets of the one big experience, elements of the one big story. This is inclusive practice.

The feeling that goes with fusing is *empathy.* To empathise with another is to practice a compassionate medicine. It is at the heart of healing relationship. To get stuck in empathy is another matter. Depending upon our own *susceptibility;* we bear the dis-ease too. We take it on, as if we know how it is. We don't. When this happens, if we can get interested instead, the stuckness dissolves.

Getting alongside another, empathising with another, implies free movement back to ourselves. It means we need to embody our own experience. We are not intending to be the same as another, but similar. This is the healing principle; similarity. *Like cures like.* A homeopathic remedy and a homeopathic relationship is similar to the dis-ease state not the same as it.

When we get stuck in empathy we feel so much for the other. We are moved by their story. We feel the unspoken suffering so much that we can no longer act as witness to it. We are unable to stay with the other and inquire with care into what is happening for them. We may assume we know already because we feel so keenly for them. We can't 'bear' it in other words.

At this point, the supervising self knows it is time to draw back and go within to find that obstacle within ourselves to staying with another.

Being specific can help: Staying with the original language of the person you are fusing with, following their specific track, will lead out of the general sense of being in the same state by asserting the characteristic differences.

Changing modalities can be helpful. If you are stuck in empathetic feeling for example, switching to 'thinking' or 'sensing' or 'intuiting' can get you back on the other's track. 'I feel so much pain in the room' for example can dissolve in asking

"What is your sense of what is happening?" (See 'Exercising the Elements' in Chapter Four.)

Taking the time to attend to our own *felt sense* in a natural, simple way during the conversation helps. Actively listening to ourselves as well as to the other is an inclusive practice that mitigates against losing oneself completely.

Writing the conversation out afterwards, doing peer supervision, acting it out, can all reveal how and what we are stuck in.

On the other hand, we may have our buttons pushed and not be able to hear the other at all as a result. The case becomes entirely about our own concerns. Again, waking up to what is happening in getting interested in the specific reality of the other person gets us alongside them again.

We may perhaps feel too scared to follow. I'm not talking here of the sensitive awareness of knowing when to stay with suffering and when to rest. That is a matter of judgement for the clinically wise practitioner; a matter of knowing our own limits of competence and that of our healing art. I mean when fear prevents us getting alongside like it did with Helen. I sensed I'd join her in 'fighting and 'flighting' since I too can find it hard to stand my ground at times.

In post-clinical supervision, this is when 'sculpture' as a method of supervising is helpful; when we have a felt sense that we are not in right relationship; to a patient or client, to our art or to ourselves. This is why sculpting the drama with Helen was so helpful. It takes willingness and a few moments to do — rather longer to explain it.

Sculpting 1. (See Chapter Four, 'Ain't Gonna Die for You.')

In a group: Where are you in relation to your practice, your supervision, the client or relationship?

As I did in the Cheetah story, place others where they are in relation to you. How far or near is the client, for example, from you?

What is happening at that distance?

What is the felt sense?

And if you moved closer or farther away?

What are your postures in relation to each other?

And if you did it so or thus?

What is the quality of the relationship sculpted like this?

What characterises it?

What happens to it if you move it like this or this?

By yourself with a doodle pad: Scribble the relationship as stick people or just as circles in relation to each other. This can afford an instant 'aha' moment in drawing attention, literally, to the dynamic.

Students who were asked to draw the triad of themselves — patient — supervisor could see easily the shape they were making and help themselves to resolve difficulties in relationship in then drawing people closer or putting some distance between themselves and the other(s.)

Aesthetic Distancing and Inclusion

Creating an *aesthetic distance* enables us to stay with an expereince without becoming engulfed by it — it contains a supervisory quality of looking — being in it and seeing ourselves in it. (S. Jennings, 1998, pp. 115–117; Landy, 1986, pp. 98–100)

This *distance* is not an emotional coldness but rather a transcendence created by an artistic, metaphorical expression. In homeopathic practice this is the potentised remedy. The remedy is as if a metaphor for the dis-eased state.

In *dynamic supervision* the metaphor is the story telling in another mode; drama, drawing, mapping, writing, use of play figures, modelling clay, human sculpture, sand play, cartoon drawing etc. I call this *art-play*. (See

'Let's Go Fly a Kite,' 'Ain't Gonna Die for You,' 'Vital Kit' and below.) For example:

Treasure Island.

Bring to mind a person who has come to you for help.

Imagine you and this person are alone together on a desert island; a cartoon island; a patch of land with one palm tree, perhaps a treasure island, in warm or in shark infested waters, perhaps a rescue or a pirate ship on the far horizon?

What happens?

Without censuring, let your fancy roam free.

What is the story?

What is revealed to you in this cartoonish re-creation of your relationship?

What is the treasure and where does it lie?

Who has charge of it? How is it (to be) discovered?

When we are either stuck in empathy or unable to get alongside another, we can get interested instead in the patterning, the form, the shape, the image, the sound, the poetry being shown to us. It is not to close our hearts to another. It is to walk along with them awhile inquiring

"Is it like this? Or this?"

It is being free to move back and forth between ourselves and the other, like sand in an hourglass continually turned about; now full of our own concerns, now empty and receptive. Or like a tai chi walk; one leg raised and empty, the other grounded and full.

This inclusive movement enables us to move freely between self knowledge, knowledge of the other and knowledge of the art.

If we are too person centred, then we can discount our own story, and in unawareness of it, affect the relationship anyway. If we be too self centred; narcissistic, we see everybody else in relation to ourselves. We can be too scientific too in the sense of seeing everyone in relation to our developing maps and models. In this way other people become case objects.

A 'relational,' 'practice centred' or inclusive perspective takes in the sweep of continual movement from self, to other and the space between. (See

Introduction, An Inclusive Approach — Person to Practice Centred and Gilbert & Evans, 2000)

A Systems Perspective

Supervision means literally 'over view.'

Each person and relationship under inquiry belongs to its own system. The client to their family and community and world view, just to simplify it. The practitioner to theirs including their artistic perspective. The supervisor to theirs. With a systems approach we can start anywhere in the matrix and recover the story gradually, bit by bit.

It is the same with the individual as system: We can start with what is characteristic about the finger nail — it is ridged or flaky or spotted, and move around the body, mind, feelings, e-motions, delusions, cravings and aversions, dreams and fears etc. following the thread of the story. How does one symptom correspond to another? We can start anywhere and end up with the whole story.

In creating this whole experience at an aesthetic distance, we can see and experience the drama of our lives for what it is. We can see it more clearly.

The Cheetah story allows me to explore the 'system' Helen lives in. It brings my awareness to the bigger picture and reminds me to explore the whole territory, to take account of aspects of the story not formerly presented or noted by either of us.

'Cheetah' is a powerful metaphor. It is persuasive. It could lead me to prescribe it as a remedy for Helen and so miss the point. Its purpose is to highlight the 'fight and flight' dilemma. Helen's sense of being ungrounded and disconnected starts to make sense as part of this systemic inquiry. (See Chapter Six, 'And the Boat Capsized in Deep Water.') We tend naturally to maintain the systems we live in, biological, social and spiritual. This tendency to homeostasis links to our instincts for survival. (See Chapter Seven, 'The Dog's Story.') In therapy we might name this resistance to change.

Going with Resistance

A homeopathic approach to supervision is a principled way to meet with resistance to changing anything about the systems we live in. Change and adapt we must in order to survive, thrive and flourish. Tell that to Helen with her back against the abyss or to Phil as he holds onto the icy ledge by his finger tips to stop himself falling into the abyss. (See Chapter Seven, 'The Dog's Story.')

The homeopathic way is the path of least resistance; 'getting alongside' another, in an energetic echo of the moves being made. This proves to be such a powerful act of itself that change very often occurs quite naturally and most gracefully as a result. When I 'got alongside' Helen's terror I could feel my response to it and see how different hers was. I was no longer 'fused' with her. For me in that moment a cheetah mother, for her the sun and stars — almost pure hydrogen.

Expect the Unexpected

The image of the cheetah came to me in acting out the drama of my relationship with Helen, in being really present to the experience. It didn't bring me to Helen's remedy. It gave me back the freedom to move from the fixity of either running or fighting, showing to me a third way; staying with *what is* and roaring out it's name.

Supervision as a quality of looking points up the task of *re-framing* questions brought to it. We bring 'stuck' cases, which in the looking, are seen in a new light. We leave with something more and other than we came in with — something unexpected — an interrupted story. This is what we see in the next chapter…

AIN'T GONNA DIE FOR YOU

Don't shoot the messenger! Group Supervision 2

CHAPTER FOUR

Beverly is very sick. She has come to homeopathy as a last resort. Sam, her homeopath is asking:

How can I help?

Where do I go next now that the remedy is not holding?

Can homeopathy save her?

The story comes from a facilitated weekend group supervision of nine practitioners in which there was time for participants to explore working together. (See Chapter Three, 'Cheetah,' and Contracting in 'Vital Kit, Working Relationship.')

Sam is seeking supervision from one of the group while the others are either 'shadowing' or 'observing' the action (see 'Vital Kit, Guides For Triading' and 'Contexts,' Live Group Clinical Supervision). He has prescribed the remedy *Mercury solubilis* (Quicksilver, proved by Hahnemann) for Beverley, who, in her forties now, has been in an anorexic state, more or less, for over thirty years. After such a long time, decay is evident in an ulcerative colitis and indolent mouth ulcers. These are the 'facts' about Beverley. We know nothing else of her story at this stage.

At one point in his story Sam makes the gesture of opening his arms out while saying

"I am feeling overwhelmed "

He goes on

"'Not just by Beverley — If I'm not there for people all the time; and in the way they need me to be, they may not come back and I need them to come back. But if I carry on like this, I won't help anyone I will get sick instead"

At this point the person 'shadowing' Sam emphasizes his gesture. She stands with her arms spread, as if martyred on a cross and takes the risk of saying:

"I will die for you."

Sam is startled by the stark image of martyring himself. Seeing it afresh as a gesture is a revelation to him. He looks to the 'shadow' and in a stronger voice emphasises

"I'm <u>not</u> going to die for you!"

Later, in 'feedback' from the observers who become a 'Greek chorus,' so to speak, for the presenter, this becomes a group refrain as first one then another picks it up. (see 'Vital Kit, Contexts,' Live group Clinical Supervision). A song emerges which is eventually chanted, roared, drummed, stomped and sung out as the group finds it voice; listening and responding to each other like this:

"Ain't gonna die for you.

Take my pain it will be your gain

Ain't gonna die for you

If you cure my pain your purse will gain

Ain't gonna die for you

Take your money? Don't be funny

Ain't gonna die, Ain't gonna die, Ain't gonna die for you!"

The group getting up and moving round the room, picking up musical instruments, shaking tambourines, stomping feet, clapping hands, finding the refrain and the rhythm.

The importance of the irreverent, outrageous and one sided song, concentrating as it does on one refrain, is that, like the shadow's enlargement of Sam's gesture, it both potentises the case and gives Sam a distance from it (*Aesthetic distance,* see 'Cheetah'). He can see it and experience the absurd in it. The song also spontaneously echos the foolish and mischievous aspects of the mercury state, beginning in this way to contact it's childlike and transformative possibilities. Beverley is 'dissolving' herself in anorexia to the point of now breaking down her tissues. Can she 'escape' from the mercury state and recover herself? What have Sam's problems in practice to do with her?

Just talking about what he is doing and what he could do instead, only has the power of

"I see. I will try harder next time to do it differently."

Beverley too has been trying harder to do it differently for thirty years with little success. This can perhaps reinforce the fantasy of being the perfect and therefore paralysed one in the face of dis-ease saying

"This shouldn't be happening,"

rather than

"What is happening?"

A song and homeopathically prescribed remedy, however, have the power to *move* us: A song to shift Sam's awarenes and. a homeopathic remedy to shift the pattern of dis-easing.

Back in the triad (story teller, active listener and observer(s), see 'Vital Kit, Guides for Triading') Sam reflects on the way in which his practice has become his persecutor and he it's victim and it's martyr. His cry of

"I'm not going to die for you"

becomes

"And I'm not killing you either!"

The *Mercury* Message

Sam has brought his work with Beverley to supervision and almost immediately side tracks into his own general response to practice. He is talking directly however to Beverley's unspoken *Mercury* fantasy of killing and being killed as expressed through her chronic anorexia — literally killing herself, she experiences it as being done to her — she has no power over it.

Sam concludes that he has lost his balance in practice because he has been motivated by fear of losing patients, and therefore his fragile income. In his fantasy he has to fix everything and be quick about it. Sam echos Mercurius Solubilis in his hurried desire to tell all about his practice and to 'fix' everyone quickly. He likes a tidy practice with right remedies and fast responses. He is slow himself to respond to patients; takes a long time considering remedies and then worries they aren't right. (See Norland, 2003 for the story of Mercury and the differences between *Mercurius solubilis* and *vivus*.)

In practicing from fear he is losing the art of responding homeopathically to Beverley. Fear is keeping him from *getting alongside* her, preoccupied as he is with his own concerns. Fear means he can't trust responding to her with a similar, energetic and minimal response. Prescriptions are starting to chase this symptom and that in a random and desperate attempt to stop the progress of the ulcerative disease. Again, Mercury's impulsive movements towards escape are mirrored in Sam's reactions.

The active listener in the triad *models* for Sam the redemptive power of being heard. Making a space for reflection instead of rushing in to 'fix' things; models the equilibrium so lacking in *Mercurius,* the barometer of remedies. The shadow's risky intervention models an energetic and minimal response with the power to shift Sam's stuck feelings about his practice rapidly, gently and as we shall see in a lasting way.

The story continues…

I got to thinking again about this supervision while listening to a radio play about an angel who came to earth. In my relaxed state, Hermes, the winged messenger of the Gods, the Roman Mercury, and the refrain from the supervision group came together in a question:

"In what way <u>do</u> we die every day in practice?"

Up came the response. *"Dying to ourselves."* In dying to or forgetting ourselves, we let go of fruitless and morbid responsibility for the suffering of another. In its place comes a true compassion in which we are free to act without guilt and with full use of our sensibilities. It is a kind of dissolving of the self into the act of being in the moment. This polarity in *Mercury* is expressed as dissolving into death and destruction at one extreme and dissolving separation at the other. "The theme of the dissolution of form leading to death is easy to find in *Mercurius,* while the opposite, new beginnings leading to life, is the promise which healing holds out." (Norland, 2003)

Shooting the Messenger

Shooting the messenger for bringing bad news is not the way we want to *'die'* for our patients,

"If you can't cure me of my suffering and be quick — and cost effective about it — then you are fired!" or

"I will try to alleviate you of your symptoms (messengers of the dis-eased state) without looking at the bigger picture. I won't practise my craft so much as abuse my art!"

Correspondence

What is this disease? How is it being expressed? What is it like? What in the world is like it?

Any sign or symptom is a signal, an attempt to raise awareness: A hot and flushed face may indicate fever which may indicate in turn several possibilities; over heating, dehydration, infection etc. A recurrent dream or unbidden fancy may be trying to bring something important to consciousness. (See Chapter Seven, 'The Dog's Story.')

A vital practice is an inquiring one.

In relating the individual story to the bigger picture, a correspondence is made. There is a connection between the dis-ease and being in the world. Instead of an aberration that needs be fixed, the diseased state is recognised as one of the myriad creations of the universe. It may not be condusive to life. It may be that death is what is required. We don't know.

A vital practice isn't a death defying one. We do use our craft and all our wily ways to defy death and we do allow it to be part of the picture too.

Homeopathic remedies are bigger stories into which we write our own. Ancient myths and legends too; our universal stories, connect our ordinary lives with mythic journeying.

In relating Sam's story to the myth of Hermes, we can see it in the light of an archetypal struggle; Hermes as the messenger from the Gods is bearing knowledge.

What are we being told?

In relating it to the bigger picture, Sam's becomes a shared story and as such we feel compassion for him. We don't judge him for fusing with aspects of Beverley's state or for being too fearful or too this or too that.

"We would do it differently. That wouldn't happen to us. Why don't you do it like this or that — like me?"

We see Sam's story as just one version of a universal one we each tell in our own ways. We accept it as such. (I'd have liked to have made the connection with the Hermes story at the time of the supervision for it may have been helpful…but that's another story.)

Stories include the maps we bring to practice: Miasms, meridians, charkras, constellations and Mappa Mundi. (See Chapter Six, 'And the Boat Capsized in Deep Water.') These represent the bigger picture, the bigger story into which we write our own and thereby make sense of it. The remembering is, they are just maps. They are not the territory as the saying goes. They show us to ourselves. They help us make meanings. They join us to the collective. They are pathways to our unconscious processes. And when all said and done, they too are only stories.

Stories we tell ourselves

I could help if he was more open, if she wasn't on the pill, if the husband came for help, if only she'd listen…

If only I tried harder I would get the right remedy/response/treatment plan.

A healing art is a vocation and that means not getting paid enough to live on.

A healing art is a profession and that means getting paid like a lawyer.

What stories do you bring to your practice?

How else could they be told?

Write a song, a limerick, a ditty, or a dreadful doggerel, making it as silly as possible, telling the stories you bring to practice.

The Group Story

In telling our stories in a group, whether that is a self help group, a therapeutic one, an addiction recovery group, a supervision group or any other group meeting to promote change, we connect with the collective story. We each become a unique part of it, entering into both personal and group change. The group context can be a potent experience in re-creating the individual state, the group state and that of the wider context. (Thompson, 1999)

The dreadful ditty in Sam's case possibly reflects a part of the homeopathic community's collective story of insufficiency, for example: Not enough money, not enough time, not enough knowledge; we need more remedies, etc. This would be Psoric Miasm in Hahnemann's mapping of chronic disease. (1828) The group is relating to the aspect of the story they are most susceptible to. *Mercury,* with its unstable movement between dissolving boundaries and destroying itself, is primarily a 'syphillitic' remedy —and an old school medicine for acute syphillis infection.

The group didn't choose to sing that song. It arose spontaneously from the dramatic re-creation of Sam's story. It was the part of his story the group was susceptible to at that moment if you like. It was the part they could recover from at that moment.

As social beings, we make the meaning of our lives in relationship to others. Group work is a microcosm with potential to reflect and transform our world. We hear our stories in a myriad of ways. We can get the group behind us to support our fragile voice and sing out our story with us.

Can you tell a story from your own life that took a number of other people to help make?

A story of learning something perhaps?

Who was there? What happened?

Who made their presence felt by their absence?

Who would you have liked to be there or wish hadn't have been?

How could the story about how you learn be different? How would it involve other people?

Group Supervisions

Group dynamic supervisions can heighten the vital experience of practice. (See Chapter Three, 'Cheetah.') A group is more than the sum of its parts. It can make an as *if one voice.* In homeopathy, the group is elemental to our knowledge of material medica. Provings are the collective story telling of the effects of medicinal substances. Each prover contributing their own unique experience of the matter.

A group can be a powerful source of awareness then as well as of healing; heightening and dissolving separation. Non verbal and minimal verbal communications, as well as group storytelling, tend to potentise and cohere the group voice as in this story chapter.

As a potent force for change, it follows that a group can contribute to dis-easing as much as to healing. As in any other relationship, clarifying intention is a good starting point.

The Urge to Merge and the Need to Separate

In every group there is an 'urge to merge' and a 'need to separate.' *Mercury* is one version of this — the ability of the crude metal to absorb other metals and yet return to its own state unchanged. For both group and metal it is the dynamis, the motive force, that counts: What do we move towards and away from and how? Keeping these tendencies in view helps to see what the group as a whole and any individual in it is doing.

What is happening now is what needs to be acknowledged by the group and/or the facilitator. (Houston, 1984; Nitsun, 1996; Thompson, 1999; Proctor, 2000 and see Contracting in 'Vital Kit, Working Relationship.')

It can be a good idea to check in with how much you are needing to be a part of the group, or apart by yourself, at the start of any new group or meeting.

Checking in at the start of a group can be effectively done in sculpting. It works like this :

On entering the room and without words, place yourself in relation to the centre of the room, as representing the heart of the group.

Check in with yourself.

Do you need to lie down and rest?

Stand your ground?

Sit and wait for the group to come together?

Be near or at the center?

At the edge or even back out of the room?

Near to others or apart?

Once you have found your starting place, the next thing to do is to find your voice in that place.

"I am lying here, apart and at the edge. I am tired by my journey here and am resting before I join in. / I am standing here, standing my ground. / I don't want to lose what I am bringing in the interest of joining the group. / I am sitting here at the centre. I have been waiting for this group. / I am looking forward to being here. / I'm a bit apprehensive about all this – 'doing' things, making a fool of myself. / This is just daft!"

You can then try swapping places and see how open or not you are to being there. Give voice to what that is like.

This needn't take much time and you can get down to the task of supervising each others practices with more knowledge of the mistrust in the room; the willingness, energy and ability to work together.

Group numbers affect the energetic potential. Seven to nine tends to be an optimum number for dynamic work. There are enough different people and yet not so many that there is little chance of being inclusive.

Three practitioners can do group dynamic supervision in that there is always at least one observer to draw attention to what is happening now. (See 'Vital Kit, Guides for Triading.') In using empty chair, plasticine, paper and pens — and imagination alone, one can do dynamic work too. (See Activities in Chapter Three, 'Cheetah,' below and 'Vital Kit, Contexts,' Self Supervising.)

Making it Work:
Facilitation as Story telling — The Story of Sleeping Beauty

A facilitator's is a skilled and experienced task of holding and articulating the group process, whether this is a rotated task in a peer situation or a role allocated to a specific facilitator as is more likely to be the case in a student context. In either case, preparation, practice and guidance for the role is a pre-requisite.

Vital practice, that is work of a transforming nature, always encounters resistance to change. (See Chapter Three, 'Cheetah,' Going with Resistance.)

It is therefore wise to employ trained and experienced guides for the work in general and for doing dynamic supervision in particular. We would not think of practicing with clients without training and experienced guidance after all.

And what kind of training? I am reminded of the relevance of consciousness raising groups of the 1970s. In a feminist context, these were groups in which we came together to tell our stories to each other in order to 'wake up' to the reality of our own lives. The feminist perspective became a *meta* commentary on our lives. It was one way of making sense of them.

'Waking up' to what is happening in an interaction is the supervisory task. Telling the story this way and that in order to see what kind of sense it might make as a whole. The supervisor's art as meta commentary or story telling. A narrative approach to supervisor training then could prove very useful as the group supervisor or group facilitator (regarded here as the same role) needs to articulate and hold a story while letting go into the possibility of new ones arising. A knowledge of 'bigger stories,' of myth, fairy tale and legend, forms a part of the supervisor's 'vital kit' according to this view.

"Storying turns an event into an experience." (Parry & Doan, 1994)

Holding the story in a group when so many stories arise and weave together is a mercurial affair: Can you visualise a broken thermometer? trying to retrieve those silvery blobs rolling across the floor? Gathering in the elusive quicksilver of Sam's group supervision story has come to me so slowly over almost a year of rememberings and dreamings. The facilitator or group supervisor becomes part of the group story; 'waking up' to the interaction and then being lulled to sleep again in the group experience.

The fairy tale "Sleeping Beauty" may usefully come in here as a re-membering of the supervisor's task.

Sleeping Beauty is exiled to live in a group with the seven dwarves. She is to be kept safe there, having been cursed by the thirteenth fairy who was not invited to her christening. The dwarves work, work, work all day and they are all together alive and well. Just as Sleeping Beauty reaches the age of maturity, having worked and 'stayed awake,' so to speak, all this time, she pricks her finger on the spinning wheel sent to trap her, and falls asleep for a hundred years. She is woken then by a kiss from her handsome prince.

In this tale we have sleep as a cursed unconsciousness. It is the supervisor's task to 'wake up' to the process. We also have sleep as a time of change; from childhood with the dwarves to 'waking up' to sexuality as a mature woman. This indicates something else of the task; to immerse ourselves in the experience; to get lost in it, to fuse with it, to fall asleep to it's narrative meaning and just *be* in it. Because on waking up, a change will have happened. Apollo and Dyonisus, consciousness and unconsciousness, are playing again.

The supervisor is willing to be 'exiled' from the experience of the group in order to step back and witness what is happening. It is as witness that the story is told by the supervisor. In this way, the story heard is always tentatively told. It is suggested, offered; it could be like this or like this.

Exile

The role of the supervisor parallels that of the healing artist. We walk alongside another.

> "The question of 'right attitude' to case receiving may be simply expressed and possibly even engendered thus: When I am with another in a therapeutic setting I stay outside the consulting space, so that i am present. Little 'i' referring to that aspect of self which is actively and non intrusively aware and large 'I' to that complex of memories and prejudices from which opinion and projection arise. ...I like to image a session as being like going for a walk with the other into their territory so that we are both experiencing this event together. This allows for empathy to coexist with objectivity, for they are showing me the sights, yet, if the going gets tough 'i' am there alongside them." (Norland, 1998)

The group supervisor is of course part of the story too. Fusing with the group story is natural (see Chapter Three, 'Cheetah'). We are awake to our experience. Then we fall asleep to it while the meaning of it stirs down in our souls. Then we wake up to it again, some time later and often when we least expect. *Mercury* fears the unconsciousness of sleep, being troubled by frightful dreams. What is Beverley's frightful dream from which she cannot wake? What moves her to escape into the slow killing of her anorexia? What does the anorexia express?

"I was a child actor" she says, "precocious and successful. We got rich on what I earned. Things fell apart when I was a teenager. I messed with drugs. My parents divorced. I wasn't expecting that. They have both always been good to me; no cross words for me, only for each other, like the song 'Killing me softly with his words.'"

Beverley is unable to recover herself from the now dissolving, now scattering family. *Mercury* restores her to herself. There are set backs.She recovers a little and then retreats — gets a job for the first time and then loses it, passes a stool without pain and then haemorrhages — hence Sam's questions: *"Should this be happening? What do I do now that the remedy isn't holding?"*

A supervision interaction, perhaps especially a group, is an unexpected place. We intend to bring one part of our experience to supervision — like Sam with his well thought out questions at the beginning — then we forget those as we immerse ourselves in the interaction. Later we remember them again as we will see.

Symptoms of disease are like this too. They are the re-memberings of long forgotten experience. Maybe before our life time even. (These experiences homeopaths call *miasms.*)

This *meta commentary,* or story telling, is the task of facilitation. Each group member facilitates that story telling since stories are co-created. The named facilitator is not the only one carrying the story, though it is their task to attend to the 'as if one' story in the same way the proving co-ordinator does. Without the story telling, the group tale goes untold. We have the experience in the group and then we don't know what experience it is or might be. We would not notice in this case that the remedy *Mercury* is confirmed by the group interaction and that the message is to stick with this slippery customer!

We are especially in the thrall of *echo* experience or parallel process which is why it is so important to have the meta commentator's role in any supervision exercises designed explicitly to explore the echo of a state in the group. (See Chapter Two, 'Let's Go Fly a Kite.')

Again writing this book echos this, in that I keep falling asleep in the stories in letting them tell themselves and then struggle awake to see what it is they might be telling. I have to remember to hold the story, to write a thread of commentary, linking the events recorded in each chapter, so that the story is told. On the other hand, I don't want to tell the story so tight that you don't have a chance to read it your way. I can relate to Sam's fear of killing and being killed as I struggle at times to 'tell it how it is,' not wanting to 'kill off' your story of how it is in practice or be 'killed' for bringing the unexpected or unwanted message of a story.

Getting Started

A person becomes patient becomes a case (Ryan, 2002).

When I started in practice, a group supervision more usually meant a circle of practitioners meeting for post-clinical help, each with a stack of patient's case notes on their laps, waiting their turn to present to the teacher leading the group. A patient's case notes would be read out and the practitioner would ask for help with particular aspects. Suggestions would be made, most often by the teacher together with some sharing of experience by the rest of the group. (See to Ian Townsend, 2001 for a history and development of supervision in homeopathy since the 1980s.)

Each case would tend to take a long time. Often the session would end before all the cases were heard, and while we had each benefited from the insights into another practitioner's case, our own patients' cases had sometimes not been aired. The noticing was that suggestions made to help another practitioner's case, presented this way on paper, often didn't help; a new remedy or approach would be tried and end as before in nothing changing.

This would seem to be because of two things:

First: The case presented on paper did not always represent the patient being brought. A paper case is constructed by the practitioner. Many acts of listening, observing, synthesizing and analyzing take place before a case is made.

A case is itself an artistic re-creation of the practitioner's making. We would see the practitioner and the case they had made but not inquire into the practitioner's process in making the case, other than in a rational-technical way; *"What rubrics did you use?"* for example, if it was a homeopath. *"What intervention did you make and what happened in response?"* if a counselor, for example.

We did not inquire principally into intentions, attachments, motivations, loves and fears. We didn't know what the practitioner was bringing to the case so we took their problematising of it as read. (See Chapter Three, 'Cheetah.') In short, we didn't inquire into their 'stuckness'. Any stuckness was rather presumed to lie with the case itself.

Second: The vital nature of the dis-easing was communicated in the group and yet not so often actively paid attention to. We might all be sitting there in the patient's state for all we knew, but we were asleep to the possibility. A two dimensional picture of the patient's dis-easing was often all that was available to us as we paid attention to the spoken word of the practitioner reporting the case and describing their problem as they saw it.

Paper case groups are great for developing the rational-technical aspects of practice.

An example: A homeopath is bringing the case notes of a patient she has prescribed for over many months with little or no response. In a case group supervision the practitioner would be asked to explain the case and her prescriptions and the patient's responses. The supervisor and group would then attempt to help her think through the various options and differentials between remedies. Supervision as a 'place to think' (Shipton, 1997) is a valuable space in its own right. We are generally so busy responding we don't have enough time to stop and think, let alone with the help of willing and able colleagues.

Another way to work with this case: We might see, feel, sense, intuit, the presence of this absent person being written and talked about but we might only occasionally be weird enough to check out an idea, impulse, intuition or *felt-sense* with the presenting practitioner. In a dynamic supervision as opposed to a case group it might go like this: The practitioner is asked to describe, in the present tense, her first meeting with the woman.

In an example from practice this is what happened: She remembers coming into the waiting room of a large urban clinic and asking for her by name. The woman looks up on hearing her name called, *"as if a rabbit caught in the headlights"* the practitioner says. This image puts us in mind of the remedy *Opium* and it's paralysis from fright. The patient had been given a clinical diagnosis of serious illness — as if a death sentence. She hadn't recovered from the shock of that. The remedy *Opium* 10M is given after seeing that the case agrees. The patient 'wakes up' from the fright and begins to respond to other remedies for her illness.

The 'case' is in the image conveyed by the patient in a moment's gesture and not in the reams of case notes recorded in consultation. These come in later to support or challenge an impression, to help the practitioner to think homeopathically; to ask the questions:

"What is present now?"

"How is it being expressed?"

"What is it like?"

Feedback

A tendency to stay with the rational-technical aspects of a case, rather than inquire into the whole of practice in supervision, is in part a difficulty with feedback. How do you inquire into another practitioner's process so that they do not defend themselves against you? How can I be vulnerable to your scrutiny while retaining my integrity? (See The Art of Useful Feedback in 'Vital Kit, Guides for Triading'.)

We were all too polite to judge another practitioner — to their face anyway. (See 'Shame on you' in Chapter Two, 'Let's Go Fly a Kite.')

I began to think there must be more effective, more honest, more time efficient ways of peer supervising. It seemed to me that in trying to supervise each others' *cases* instead of each other, we were missing a golden opportunity. It was *us* who were present in the room in post-clinical supervision, not the actual patient. Surely it was us who could benefit from supervision directly so that we could in turn respond with more freedom, energy and compassion in practice? And if we were there as a group, couldn't we make more use of all of us?

Another aspect of these early case based supervisions was the reliance on the expert teacher. (See Chapter Seven, 'The Dog's Story.') The focus was between the paper case and the teacher. How to re-focus onto the presenting practitioner and the process? It would certainly take the heat off the teacher and allow them a cooler, supervising role rather than that of sage; being made to prescribe for people they had never met! It would mean that the presenting practitioner would be free to develop their style rather than tend to ape or else sabotage that of the teacher in order to assert independence: What subtle and not so subtle power struggles did we witness between student practitioner and *expert* teacher?

Being willing and able to give and receive *feedback* can only be based on the understanding that we have a shared task; that we are each engaged in inquiry; in being more interested in finding out *what is* than we are in judging what isn't. (See The Art of Useful Feedback in 'Vital Kit, Guides for Triading') Supervision as a quality of looking, without attachment, with compassion. Instead of

"I am a leader; I do it my way" or *"I am a follower; I do it your way"*

we have

"What is the way in this moment?"

Feel for the way…

When we follow our hearts, let our unique perception lead the way, we do practice with energy and the shift does come.

Resources: Books

My guide in getting started, and still as relevant now, is Ram Dass and Paul Gorman, *How Can I Help?* (1986). The homeopath Miranda Castro, writing in *The Homeopath,* journal of the Society of Homeopaths (1989) inspired me to explore further within my own homeopathic modality.

In practice-centred supervision groups, rather than case based ones, we started to share the experience of engaging with our practice as it was and not with how we thought it should be.

It was refreshing, heady, dangerous and adventurous to explore what went on between patient and practitioner behind the closed door of the consulting room. We blew myths, we shared excruciating experiences, anxieties, doubts and fears and laughed like drains at our common predicaments.

We also found, in our lively play, some of the *"compassion, competence, creativity and confidence"* we needed to stay with and to respond to patients during the ups and downs of healing and dis-easing. (Proctor, 2000)

Looking for a community of ideas, I went in search of books in that wonderful nest of hatching ideas, 'Compendium' bookshop in North London (now no more) and found, over time, many still essential books for the practitioner of healing arts as well as for anyone in the helping professions (including Casement, 1985; Inskipp and Proctor, 1988; Hawkins and Shohet, 1989; Houston, 1990).

Later, the over view and clarity of Michael Carroll (1996) as well as his books with Elizabeth Holloway on training (1999) and supervision in context (1999) helped further to ground a practice-centred rather than a merely case-based supervision.

Another well-thumbed text is Steve Page & Val Wosket (1994). (See to guides for phone and e-mail supervision in 'Vital Kit, Contexts' for an application of this cyclical model.)

Useful texts for working in a group context include Bion (1973), Houston (1984), Nitsun (1996), Dalal (1998), Thompson (1999), Proctor (2000) and Chesner & Hahn (2002).

Narrative approaches to supervision (eg. Parry & Doan, 1994) and many other texts from counselling and psychotherapy, dramatherapy, especially by the splendid Sue Jennings, as well as many on reflective writing, psychodrama, voice therapy, nursing and teaching, inform and support the development of what I call a *Dynamic clinical supervision.*

These books open up whole worlds of ideas and practice to liberate us from self imposed restraints. We meet ourselves in each others' writings from experience. We put it into words for each other in different ways, extending awareness.

Writing supports our intuition, confirms practice as an art, for all the science we study, and shows us that to be artists we must be free to go within to inquire into our work — without fear of getting it 'wrong.' (See Writing Our Way into Our Stories in Chapter Five, 'Magic Glasses.')

Courses

Participating in supervision courses with practitioners working in different modalities emphasizes our common experience and task; to free ourselves to be with and to respond to each other without becoming either stuck in the mire of empathy or becoming so rational-technical that we become mere 'cases' to each other.

All the while the homeopathic approach are guides to going deeper into the inquiry:

- What is characteristic?
- What does *getting alongside* look like?
- What is the minimum dose to restore order and purpose, autonomy and relatedness?
- What is the energetic response?

Bringing it Home

I started by looking outside homeopathic theory and practice for support and guidance in developing supervision. I studied person centred counseling and integrative, relational and systemic approaches to supervision. In coming full circle, to a homeopathic way of supervising, there is a sense of coming home, of integrating practice rather than it being an eclectic thing of a little of this and a pinch of that. The sources of inspiration are diverse and the thread pulls through them all.

Stories, myths, fairy tales and legends have always been a powerful source of inspiration. The stories in this book, the exercises and commentaries, each illustrate something of the nature of a dynamic and homeopathic supervision, in which practice is inquired into and re-created with minimum, energetic and sympathetic intervention.

The term *re-creation* points up the task of re-storying practice so that the practitioner is no longer stuck for a response. It refers us to recreational as restorative too. (One of three functions of supervision — 'normative, formative and restorative.' Inskipp and Proctor, 1988)

It is very liberating, very restorative, to give voice to the many aspects of practice; to role play ourselves as 'shadow' or the client with whom we are stuck or again as the stillness of our observing selves.

> "To create one must be able to respond. Creativity is the ability to respond to all that goes on around us, to choose from the hundred possibilities of thought, feeling, action, and reaction and to put them together in a unique response, expression, or message that carries moment, passion and meaning. In this sense, loss of our creative milieu means finding ourselves limited to only one choice, divested of, suppressing, or censoring feelings and thoughts, not acting, not saying, doing, or being." (Clarissa Pinkola Estes, 1992)

Coming home to ourselves is being free to move in any direction, in any way, in the certainty we can come back to ourselves. We won't get lost. We find more of ourselves in lessening the separation between ourselves and another.

The Group Invokes the *Elemental Story*

We invoke the elemental story through singing, dancing and drumming. The drum in mythology being the vehicle with which the Shaman travels into other realms. Supervision as a recreation of shame in order to transform it connects to this shamanic idea. Both words share the same root. In shame we are 'out of shape.' In shamanic transformation we 'shape shift.' (Hewson, 1999)

In telling our stories to a supervisory listener, we hear what it is we have buried for shame. We tell them differently. They change shape and so do we.

A group supervisor's kit includes hand drums, shakers, rattles and anything that can be percussed. We tell our stories in rhythm and music to 'wake ourselves up.'

Group Orchestra without a conductor:

Pick up a drum, a shaker, a stick or beater. Take it to a place in the room you feel comfortable in. Begin to make your rhythm. This is your own rhythm and noise. Play around, try this and that, this instrument or that, THERE ARE NO RIGHT RHYTHMS. THERE ARE NO RIGHT NOISES.

When you are ready you may want to listen to the rhythm and noise of another. Perhaps move towards them. Now you are listening and responding to each other. Someone else joins you. You wander over to another pair. The group forms and reforms, perhaps eventually making a circle, jamming together. Not a musician among you and hark at that rhythm!

You begin to move to the beat. Stamp your feet. Put down your drum and clap your hands. You are the rhythm. You start a hum in your throat, a sounding in your chest, a note in your head. You sound them low, you sound them loud. Now you're cooking.

What happens?

What do you notice about yourself, the group and how you relate?

Group Orchestra or choir in a circle with a conductor

Choir:

In a circle, one participant takes the centre as conductor. Each finds their own voice and note. Sing it out. Play with it. Hold your own or respond to another or to the group as a whole. The conductor gestures for the group to swell in sound or to go quieter. She indicates to one to sing out and to the rest to stop and listen. This goes around, each one having a turn to sing out and to listen to the rest.

Another takes a turn as a conductor.

What happens?

What do you notice about yourself?

About the group as a whole?

What is this telling you about the way you relate in practice?

(See Receiving and Taking the Case in Chapter One.)

Recreating practice as human sculpture emphasizes the stuck places and moving pathways in relationships. (See Sculpting 1 in Chapter Three, 'Cheetah.')

Sculpting 2:

You are bringing a scenario from practice for some heightened awareness of what is happening; to see more clearly where you are stuck and what you might do in response. Instead of telling the story or acting it out, ask the participants to help you sculpt your drama.

Decide who you are: Practitioner, client, client's mother perhaps in the case of a child, doctor or consultant in the case, etc. (Works well in acting out family drama too.)

Now place the others at a distance and in a posture in relation to yourself.

Where are they?

What are they doing?

What is their awareness of you or feeling towards you?

How is that modeled in their posture?

Place them as you see it.

Have the commentary out loud to yourself as you place and model your sculptures.

Where would you like them to be? Doing what? Feeling what towards you?

Move them around. Play with it.

You could now give them voice. Ask them to move around in a way that expresses how it is from their position.

A dialogue starts — your sculpture starts to take on a life of its own.

What happens to your story as you sculpt it like this?

Let the Hand Do the Talking

Modelling in plasticine lets us see practice in a way we hadn't noticed before. It can strip away the *blah blah* of the *comfort story* and reveal something more primal, more elemental. (Preferably the stuff that smells like it did when we were children or when we played with our children as that helps us to play now.)

Take up some plasticine. Let your hand do the moulding as you pay attention to the person or the situation you are stuck in. It helps to lose some of that mind control if you use the less dominant hand. Don't decide how to model it. Let the hand do the rolling and kneading. When you have finished, show it to a partner. What do they see? What are they describing? Not interpreting but seeing?

Do the observations throw new light on what you are bringing?

(See Chapter Seven, 'The Dog's Story" for further inquiry into 'hands' in practice.)

These are ways in which we can 'unstick' ourselves, *interrupting* our comfort stories. In this way we make some shared sense of our lives and in so doing reconnect with ourselves and each other. In these ways we recreate the stories we bring from practice. In telling them anew in these surprising ways, we gain fresh insight into them, see what is characteristic about them and how we might freely respond.

Turning it Around – The Shape of Sam's Story – a Transforming Triad

One way we perhaps write our story as practitioners that can keep us stuck in a devitalized practice, tending to burden and 'burn us out,' is in a triangular bind: (Eric Berne, 1964)

Victim

Persecutor

Rescuer

In supervising ourselves, and perhaps especially in a group supervision, where we can engage dramatically with each position, we can re-create this so:

Vulnerable

Potent

Reflective

In owning our own vulnerability as practitioners and carers, we can liberate ourselves from this persecutory — victimizing bind, creating a transforming triad instead.

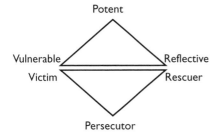

In Sam's story, he arrives feeling persecuted by his need to rescue his patients. They are also victims he needs to rescue from the clutches of disease.

In getting down to the 'elemental' story; fear of killing and being killed, poverty and death, Sam begins to own his vulnerability. In owning this he regains his freedom to move…

The Hero? Another Shaping of Sam's Story

There is another archetypal image floating about this story and at the risk of mixing metaphors and losing the plot, I would like to explore Sam's story from another angle. (The chapter is writing itself in a mercurial way — slippery!)

There is a story told by Peter Nicholls in *Journey for Madmen* (Nicholls, 2001) in which he says lone sailors are guided by what he calls the *'Ulysses Principle'*: (referring to a book by J.R.L. Anderson called *The Ulysses Factor*) They are making heroic journeys; taking the risk of breaking up in a storm, of death by drowning. Nicholl's book is an *Homeric simile* for the journey we make in healing relationship, in that sailing alone around the world, is above all else, an odyssey of self discovery.

I was preoccupied with sailing as a metaphor for the relationship between practitioner and client at the time of the group supervision recorded here and the one -to-one sessions in Chapter Six, 'And the Boat Capsized in Deep Waters.'

Sailing logs record emotional and mental states as much as wind and weather. The well being or otherwise of the sailor, as much as the boat. While cheerful messages are radioed to family and media, the log tells the real tale: Trail blazing lives; Chichester, Knox Johnson, Chay Blythe and Donald Crowhurst.

In the story told by Nicholls of the first Golden Globe solo race round the world, Donald Crowhurst discovers that he is too frightened to return home to bankruptcy and shame and too realistic to go on with the race in an ill prepared and leaky boat. Bankruptcy he can put a brave face on. Shame he cannot. The knowledge that he has deluded himself and others into the belief that he could sail alone round the world is too much to bear. He finds he can't move either way. So he stays in the Atlantic, and in these days before satellite, he sends radio messages falsifying his course and lying about his speed. He makes it up, and in losing hold on his own reality, disaster strikes. The true state of his unravelling mind he records in the daily ship's log.

Adventurous lives. Heroic lives. Visceral adventure. Grappling with the elements. The terror of sitting atop a 40 foot wave in a storm, or rolling over, hatches open, the deep flooding in. I have never been there, yet I know that fear. And as I read, I revisit it. I feel my stomach tighten then drop, I am sick with fear. Relief floods my veins as the boat rights itself and the stars shine once more through the parting storm clouds. I breathe easily and deeply, I am happy. Life has returned.

I know that fear and that deep sighing contentment. Life flooding in.

Introverts and extroverts go to sea. That isn't the difference. They have friends and family. That isn't it. They are people like us in these ways. In other ways they are extraordinary. Extraordinarily courageous in being driven to physical extremes in order to experience being fully alive.

They express for the rest of us, those living ordinary lives, something of our own heroic task. We feel with them, suffer and rejoice, because we too meet ourselves, risking everything at times in order to do so.

The terror and joy I experience again in reading these tales largely belongs to relationship. It also belongs to physical suffering. Not the bruised battering of a great adventure on the sea but to that of disease.

As a homeopath, attempting to stay in relationship with others who are suffering in different ways, I am setting off into unknown waters with them. I don't know whether I am up to it or will know what to do to come safely home again. In trying to stay with them, I am continually up against myself, getting in the way, obscuring the view. My own questions and preoccupations can be more present than the other person:

"Are we in 'right' relationship?

Am I making the 'right' response?

Will it be any use to go on in this way?"

There is the lovely story of Bernard Moitessier, the French sailor in the race, who is shown direction by a school of porpoises when he drifts off course.

Moitessier loved being at sea, the journey for him being an end in itself. He practiced yoga and meditated daily on deck, eschewed a safety harness wherever he could and rounded the horn accompanied by the Aurora Australis, the southern lights. In a final twist to his tale, he plunged back into his journey, beginning again round the world, on finding himself in the lead and faced by the onerous prospect of a 'hero's welcome' if he returned victorious to France.

Others, consumed either by their loneliness and self doubt or else unable to face reality, were less able to respond to the ever changing conditions of such a journey. Donald Crowhurst disappeared over the side of his boat, the only place left for him to go, when both going on and turning back became too painful to consider.

Travelling with a fellow sufferer can take us both into our own deepest fears, and, into our most unconditional loving. We can each experience the highs and lows, despair and joy of the lone adventurer, and, at times experience the '*I-Thou*' moment of being at one. (Buber, 1996 ed.)

It may be an heroic journey at times. Is it however a hero's journey? Is it really heroic medicine we want to practice and heros we want to be?

It was the polarity between 'hero' and 'villain' (originally meaning a simple person rather than a wrongdoer) that fuelled the deadly competition which eventually claimed more than one of the sailor's lives in this race. (The sailors were originally sailing alone around the world independently of each other. It was only when a race for prize money was introduced that the voyage became a deadly competition between them.) The most life enhancing journey was made by Moitessier who turned his back on the hero's welcome.

How many of us have been seduced at times by the heroic model of the healer who will work tirelessly, usually alone and against great odds, to 'rescue' others? In so doing we leave our own simple selves behind and locate all that is simple and ordinary with the client as if to say,

"I have no ordinary needs for rest and refreshment, for fun and games. I can toil late into the night and think of you all my waking hours…."

So we rob the client of their own heroic journeying.

Practicing healing relationship is rarely trail blazing as in the big adventure, though the path can glow sometimes in the dark…

Odysseus Again, *Jim Kimmis*

> I need to find or make other maps
> to navigate this sea of darkness
> where sunken islands wait to capsize
> my fragile craft. Skeletons of ships
> beneath my keel are warnings of loss,
> evidence of foundered enterprise
>
> that glow greenly among dim outcrops
> of basalt, column-stumps of temples
> taken by the waves. I'm out of time,
> driven by a storm-demon that strips
> my sails to tatters, a wind that chills
> my shuddering bones with its sublime
>
> indifference to my earthly corpse
> and all its weaknesses. Rudderless
> and breaking up, this vessel of mine
> has no destination but collapse,
> no purpose but to survive the curse
> of a hostile ocean. The grey line
>
> of the horizon mocks me with hopes
> of reaching a safe harbour, peoples
> my vision with a mirage of bright
> towers and strong walls. Delusion shapes
> a future for me while the tide pulls
> me dawnward, through an uncharted night.

Sam regains his potency in exploring the shadowy aspects of his practice. He realizes he too 'needs to find or make other maps to navigate this sea of darkness.' In coming up to the light again he sings out that he has no intention of either killing or being killed. That which has to die is of quite another order; his own self-consciousness as an heroic prescriber. That vessal 'has no destination but collapse.' Neither did Beverley kill her family and neither does she need to die for them. The guilt the child of divorced parents can carry has kept her childish and dependent, so serving to keep them together in a way for her sake. Well met by Mercury, she begins to let go of them and to recover herself.

Sam parallels this recovery. In re-membering himself as an active listener, he restores his freedom to move and respond to Beverley. He can consider how he practices and how he values that work. He starts to put himself and his art at the centre of his story, and as he does so, he regains his energy and works again with compassion.

Now he asks the questions

"What is happening now?"

"How is vitality being expressed?"

"What is the most similar, vital and minimum response to support the direction already taken?"

Instead of those he came in with:

How can I help?

What do now that the remedy is not holding?

Can homeopathy save her?

Supervision Re-frames the Question

Supervision most often 're-frames' questions so that we can move with them where we were previously stuck.

In getting back to simple observation and responding from first principles, the way ahead begins to show itself.

Sam arrived in a place of forgetting; lost in the thrall of the experience. He loses himself then in the dynamic supervision, and in so doing, re-members what he used to know. He 'wakes up' to his task. He forgets himself. His focus is entirely on the patient. He brings his clinical wisdom to bear. He re-prescribes *Mercury solubilis* in the daily LM potency and the case moves. (LM being Hahnemann's final refinement of the homeopathic potency scale for rapid, gentle and permanant healing.)

The subject of the next chapter is re-membering and dis-membering the stories we bring to practice, of who we are and who we must be...

MAGIC GLASSES

Re-Vision

CHAPTER FIVE

Supervision is a quality of looking. It is interrupting our stuck narratives of *"this should be like this"* and *"that should be like that."* It is looking at what is happening without fear or favour. Except of course we do fear. We do favour. Waking up to our loves and fears is what supervision is all about. (Shohet, 2002)

In becoming more aware of what we are attached to; more accepting of where we are, we are freer to respond homeopathically;

Uniquely — adapting to each new situation.

Vitally — responding to what's important, what motivates.

Similarly — getting alongside the other/ the situation.

Minimally — doing just enough to restore freedom to move.

Supervision is an 'outsider' perspective; a meta view.

If I am right in the middle of the practice, the organisation, relationship or case I am looking at, I can't see the wood for the trees. I am too much a part of the culture.

A supervisory way of looking is to stand outside of ourselves too. It is "I" watching "my" intervention or desire or aversion, etc. A good working relationship with ourselves is what we need to make the most of supervision. It means the looking will tend to be appreciative, compassionate and reflective rather than persecutory, victimising or rescuing.

Supervision is about change. While the task is to accept what is happening — a reality check— it is with an eye to moving on; and change is trailing loss.

Necessary Loss

Each time we move we lose something; the habitual way of doing something, the comfort story; that worn out way of relating we are so attached to. To be alive is to keep on moving. Adaptation and change are necessary to survival.

Peter, who works with adults with profound learning disability, tells how it is when they explore the necessary losses change brings.

"All I'm ever after is for people to remember something. If they can re - member what happened perhaps they can move on. We play with remembering silly things. If it's fun, they are going to remember it. The bereavement group is all based on games. 'Find the lady' — put a sweet under one of three cups and move it around. It isn't where you thought it was. It has moved. It's all about change. Even minute change can be really hard. We make a game of it; losing and finding the sweet. Watch the anxiety turn to excitement; "Where is it this time?"

Loss of comfort:

How about physical comfort?

What do you have to do to experience a little physical discomfort? Just to stretch the boundary of what you need to be comfortable. Why?

It can help to get us outside ourselves — to see ourselves as 'other' and in being less attached, leave us freer to move.

A cold instead of a warm shower in the morning?

Walk to work instead of drive?

Sit with hunger pains instead of immediately reach for food?

Drink a glass of water instead of coffee or biscuit?

When really busy, sit still, perfectly still for five minutes and do nothing more?

What could you do to remember what your physical comfort is attached to?

Try unhooking from the routines — try one hook a day — notice what happens…

In getting outside of our comfort zone in this way we are freer to move; less attached to our own personal maintenance culture — and that gives insight into the supervisory way — where we can see how it is and see how else it might be.

Peter continues

"Toy glasses; you know these eyes on springs? They are our magic glasses to see into the future. When we put them on in the bereavement group we can move on; see what we want to do and who we want to be.

Margo says she wants to be tall and dark and go to live in Spain. I don't yet know what this means to her. What 'Spain' is. It gets her seeing something she isn't being now. Is it getting more aware of who and where she is by seeing who she isn't? It's small. You have to grasp at anything…

There's one guy in the group who would do anything you ask him to do. No matter what. A couple of weeks ago in the group I said "Would you put your coat on we are going swimming now?" He said, " No, I don't want to go swimming." That was amazing enough. He doesn't usually have anything to say let alone a refusal. I said, " Why don't you want to go swimming? Give me one good reason and we won't go."

"It's too bloody cold." He says. Brilliant. That's what these magic glasses are about. When you've got these on you can try pushing the boundary of who you might be — someone who knows what he wants maybe."

Put the magic glasses on. The plastic bits go over your ears and they dig in a little. They sit a little above the bridge of your nose. The springs droop and weigh as you nod your head. Close your eyes. You look very silly. It isn't possible to be serious with these on.

What can you see? These are magic glasses. What does your world look like? Who are you in it?

What happens when you meet other people?

Who are they to you?

And you to them?

What would you like to say? Or do?

The magic glasses, in their silliness, can free us to play with our stories and notions of who and where we are, what we can and cannot do. Peter plays with the magic glasses as a way into the hitherto unexpressed worlds of the people in his care. It is his way of *actively listening* to people without the practice of regular conversation.

Peter says

"All I am ever after is for people to remember something."

Re-membering as putting ourselves back together again; gathering in the discarded limbs, the parts of ourselves we have dis-membered over the years. (See The Handless Maiden in Chapter Seven, 'The Dog's Story.')

'Square pegs in round holes' we say when we squeeze ourselves into lives that don't fit. Where do we fit in our lives and where have we to cut this part off and that to meet the task?

What do we censure of ourselves in order to meet the task of practitioner/ supervisor/ teacher/ parent etc.

What do we deem unacceptable?

What do we know that we suppress?

What have we forgotten that we used to enjoy doing?

What were we going to be when we grew up?

What desire did that express?

How is that expressed now in our lives?

Every relationship has its tasks. (See Carroll 1996 for tasks of supervision.) Remembering the task and seeing that we are fit to do it is a vital practice. Clarifying intention on this, or as Page and Wosket (1994) put it, contracting, is the work itself practically done.

Re-membering and Naming the Task

When we are supervising we intend to re-member our practice. When we are practising our healing art we intend to forget division and promote integrity. Learning happens when we practice a healing art. Healing happens when we do supervision. We do the task of either supervising or practicing our healing art. We don't *do* one in place of the other — we remember the task.

The last thing we want when we come to supervision is for the supervisor to start pathologising us. Clarifying intention at every point is the top and bottom of ethical relationship after all. We are vulnerable when we share our work and relationships in supervision — we have come to learn more about what we do, not to be turned into patients or therapy clients.

When we come as therapy clients or as patients, we come to recover something of ourselves. Some of us choose the path of 're-membering' and some of us the path of 'forgetting' in doing this. That is, some of us want more conscious connection with where we are and some of us want just to 'forget' the dis-ease and move on. The point is to be clear about the task; to recover. Unwanted insights are as unhelpful as attempting to remedy supervisees. On the other hand, keeping information, stories and connections from patients and clients who want to know, can be just as unhelpful or even a downright abuse of power.

Learning from Experience

We can't remember what we don't experience authentically in the first place. In order to learn from our practice, we had better have our experience rather than the one we have told ourselves we should be having or the one we have just had or think we may have in a minute. (See Presence in Chapter Two, 'Let's Go Fly a Kite.')

If we look at our early learning, we can perhaps see what it is we tend do with our own experience.

Experience of Learning

What do you know about how you learn? Can you close your eyes and remember an early learning that was hard? What is the story of that?

Who was there?

What happened?

What was hard about it?

Write down the story of an early and hard learning experience.

What about an early and pleasurable or fun learning?

Do you remember an instance of that?

What is the story?

Write it down.

In remembering your stories; hard and pleasurable, what are the qualities of each? How are they different from each other? How similar?

Is positive feedback always necessary for example or can we learn well and happily from negative feedback, as nature does, doing what works until it doesn't and then developing another course? (Hawkins, 2002)

What are you noticing about your attachment to 'strokes' and your attitude to critical feedback?

What about fun and silliness? What role do they play?

Can you find out from these stories what it is you need in order to learn?

Is it hands on experience?

To be shown?

To find out by yourself?

To be supported? How?

To read about something?

To practice?

To be encouraged?

To feel into it?

To think then do?

To do then review?

How do you learn?

This is an exercise to do on your own. It also benefits from sharing. Each helping the other to notice the attachments and the patterns.

What of obstacles to learning? Ah, here's the rub. Even before we get to our optimum conditions for learning, there is resistance to learning. Shame is a big obstacle for many of us. (See Shame On You in Chapter Two, 'Let's Go Fly a Kite.')

'Can't' scripts

"I'm ashamed to ask. I should know by now." (should and oughta)

"I can't listen because I'm already supposed to know aren't I?" (Expert)

"I can't begin to learn to swim because I can see how difficult the triple somersault dive is." (Non starter)

"I can't learn French because I'm not a natural with languages." (Self limiter)

"I can't learn math because I'm a right brainer" (Concept as limitation)

"I can't practice healing relationship because I'm not yet healed." (Who is?)

What are the stories you tell yourself about what and why you can't learn?

Brainstorm all the things you tell yourself you can't learn and all the reasons why you can't learn them. Now, put your magic glasses on...

Forgetting

We forget ourselves when we are well. We are at ease with ourselves and the world. We can move freely from place to place and person to person without falling apart, still recognisable as ourselves, even as we adapt to different situations. We may feel vulnerable, hopefully we can. We may feel ashamed, embarrassed, exposed, irritated, angered, humoured, undone by love. Hopefully we can. We are still ourselves. The outside and the inside of us are in some sort of conversation anyway.

When we are not so well, not ourselves as we say, it is as if we are separated from ourselves. The inside and the outside of us no longer talk together. Outside I may seem a small mouse haired silent woman, always hugging myself for warmth. Inside I toss my long dark hair and stride out into the sunlight.

Who Needs Practice?

Active listening is practising a meditative quality of attention; noticing all that passes without attempting to intervene in it. Practitioners who are suffering a bereavement for example, will often say that they want to return to practice sooner rather than later — not always but often. One reason would seem to be that the quality of attention given to another in any healing art is balm to the listener as is it to the receiver of the attention.

Practice is a still point in our mind busy lives. To practice in a more supervisory way, actively listening without attachment, can be as healing for practitioner as it is for client. To turn it right around, if practice is not healing, not nourishing, not life affirming for practitioner as well as for client, why do it at all? Who needs it?

There is Nothing Outside of Ourselves — Healing is Self Healing

We truly meet another at the level we meet ourselves.

Too painful to recover that part of ourselves?

Too painful then to go there with another.

Too embarrassing to own that weakness?

Too embarrassing then to allow that weakness in another.

That side of me goes against my idea of who a practitioner or supervisor should be?

Then that side of you goes against my idea of who a client or supervisee should be.

Remembering who we are, what has made us, shaped us, who we have told ourselves we are and who we are not, who is 'us' and who is 'them', allows us to see just how conditionally we love ourselves — and others.

Forgetting ourselves leaves us free to see what is happening and to be whoever we want to be in response. It is as if we have our magic glasses on.

This is ethical practice in that we see ourselves in others and them in us. We aren't so divided by appearances, history, gender, sexuality, abilities. We aren't so separated and paradoxically we are more of our unique selves.

Healing relationship is truly a self healing journey.

The Journey by Mary Oliver

One day you finally knew
what you had to do, and began,
though the voices around you
kept shouting
their bad advice —
though the whole house
began to tremble
and you felt the old tug
at your ankles.
'Mend my life!'
each voice cried.
But you didn't stop.
You knew what you had to do,
though the wind pried
with its stiff fingers
at the very foundations,
though their melancholy
was terrible.
It was already late
enough, and a wild night,
and the road full of fallen
branches and stones.
But little by little,
as you left their voices behind,
the stars began to burn
through the sheets of clouds,
and there was a new voice
which you slowly
recognised as your own,
that kept you company
as you strode deeper and deeper
into the world,
determined to do
the only thing you could do —
determined to save
the only life you could save. (In Astley ed, 2002)

Inquiry is Compassionate Medicine

Inquiring into our practice *is* inquiring into ourselves since there truly is nothing outside of ourselves. There are only the stories we bring, from our healing modalities and our own lives, through which we filter awareness of each other. Developing a 'meta' view, a supervisory view, the one watching the story making, helps us to see each other both more clearly and more compassionately. We lessen the separation between 'me' and 'you,' between 'I' and 'my' and between 'us' and 'them.' There are no 'others' only the characteristic expression we each embody, as a part of the whole.

> If 'the whole' is a play, if life is play, what part do you play in it?
>
> What parts do you play?
>
> What parts would you like to play, or used to play and do no longer?
>
> What is the play you are in?
>
> What does the play you are in tell you about the story you are making of your life?

Being more of ourselves frees up our vitality in the service of practice as well as encourages another, literally gives courage to another, to be more of themselves.

Peter doesn't know yet how Margo will express herself further in the world; what sort of conversation will develop between her selves. In bringing more of himself to his practice; classroom 'shirker', adventurer, the one playing and having fun (see Chapter Two, 'Let's Go Fly a Kite'), he is *modelling* for Margo that it is okay to live a little more.

As a homeopath, I may have told myself I am required to actively feel compassion. I may feel tired, distracted, or irritated instead. In censoring those feelings, two things at least are certain: I miss vital clues to what is happening and I am less likely to regain my compassion. (See Chapter Four, 'Ain't Gonna Die for You.')

"I" Sees with Compassion What "Me" Does in Practice

Even by ourselves we are social animals; conversing with ourselves with reference to all the many voices within and without. (See Voices in 'Vital Kit, Guides for Triading.)

How to 'contradict' ourselves, to interrupt our repetitive or *comfort* stories?

Writing Our Way into Our Stories

'Morning pages' is a good place to start. (Cameron, 1994) (See to activity in Introduction to this collection.) In letting the story 'write itself down', rather than deciding exactly what and how to write before we even pick up the pen, or start a new sentence, we discover things that happened that were outside our consciousness before. This form of reflective writing does not follow an intended cycle. (Gibbs 1988; Atkins & Murphy, 1996 for example.) These maps can come in at the beginning to organize our time and help clarify intention or later to help us reorient ourselves along the way. The suggestion is, allow yourself to get lost in the process; to feel around in the dark and confusion until a less known element arises, a voice you are less familiar with. It is in this way we realize both the fears that prevent free movement and the heart's desire that keeps us going on.

What is your heart's desire?

What feelings are roused by the question?

What shapes, images, words come to mind?

What is your heart's desire?

Write it down like a song in the morning, a hymn of praise, a lovers eulogy.

How is this desire expressed in the world?

Where would I see it? How would I know it?

Write it the way it really is.

What does your heart's desire say to it's expression in the world?

Is it as the heart would have it?

What else would the heart have it do or be?

What does you heart say? Write it down from the heart.

What is your heart's desire?

The homeopathic and supervisory way takes some courage, literally a rage of the heart, to accept all that we are.

In putting our magic glasses on, contacting our playful, uninhibited, child like selves, we can perhaps contact the courage we need to meet ourselves in every stranger.

In the next story, two 'strangers' meet. We see what happens when they try to converse in their own languages…

AND THE BOAT CAPSIZED IN DEEP WATER

Whose Story Is This Anyway?

CHAPTER SIX

Meg, a supervising practitioner comes to review her work. She is no stranger to supervision or to me as a supervisor. We have worked together regularly over many years. A comfortable working relationship then.

She begins

"I am enjoying the supervisory work I am doing. I like being reflective rather than being so responsible for the difficult decisions I make when I'm practicing."

There is a lot to unpack here already, for example how practice could be more like supervision; more reflective and therefore more enjoyable and what responsibility and decision making are for Meg. I ask her where she wants to go with this session — *"exploring the territory"'* she replies.

She continues

"I don't feel I'm quite 'there' as a supervisor. I'm forcing it. For example I was observing some practitioners in a group supervision. I wanted them to do something differently. I didn't want to just observe and tell them what I perceived. I wanted them to change what they were doing and do it like I wanted them to. I wanted to be the one to control what happened."

Staying in role? Control?

"Being in control?" I venture

"I don't know what I'm doing to help if I'm not doing that. If I just stay with what is happening, I'm afraid to stay with that....

"With..?"

"My feelings. To trust the process, like in the group; to be in role as an observer and trust the others to do it right. I can't get in touch with that. "

I realise at this point that I am concerned to be of value to Meg in the time we have. (She arrived late and is leaving early today. She travels from a distance to be here.) I am tempted to force the pace — I too want to control the session in order to get somewhere. (See to 'echo'/'parallel process' in Chapter Two.)

It seems too that we are in deep water already and I feel the need to make frequent interventions, to keep the session afloat. I check this without sharing my busy mind with Meg and just resolve to slow down and 'explore the territory' with her.

She says

"I can't trust my feelings at the moment. I am in a difficult place in my life right now. I don't go there. Work is a safe haven. I have some control there. I don't have control over what is happening elsewhere. I organise everyone else. Peer supervision, a chance to reflect, like here, rather than have to fix something, is a good break from that."

I have my permission to stay with her and stop trying to fix something!

"I had no idea we would arrive here. It is what I am bringing actually: Being unhappy means I am more controlling than ever, wanting to escape situations in which I feel I have no control and too much responsibility. It is too uncomfortable. I am too vulnerable."

"*To?*"

"*People not sharing their feelings. Leaving me out.*"

"*And your own feelings? Staying with your own feelings rather than getting into everyone else's business?*"

I feel an 'ouch' as I deliver this challenge. Too much too fast?

She picks it right up.

"*I do what I accuse others of. They don't talk to me because that way they can stay in control. I don't share my feelings. I could have said to the practitioners in the group, " When you do this I feel like or it seems like…" I tried to make them do something else instead. They wouldn't do it anyway.*" She laughs.

The tension in the room is dissolving as Meg acknowledges vulnerability. It is as if we are now drifting gently in on the tide…

The pace up to this point has been as if we were going through a rapid together — or up the creek without a paddle; some uncharted and fast flowing water anyway. The session had been scheduled as a review of work priorities; a summer sail on a mill pond — except the boat capsizes in deep waters.

I am at home with the sea as metaphor. It speaks to me. I often dream and write in images risen from the oceans.

Metaphor is a moving line in that it can take us fast to the heart of the matter. It can say things which can't be approached in other, more direct ways. Metaphor is powerful speech. It makes a vital connection. It is concerned with the nature of things, with what the matter actually is, with the 'elemental story'.

Metaphor is also a shorthand record for me in that it helps me to remember where we are – or so I think – except *every session is unique*.

I keep forgetting that while I'm all at sea Meg is exploring the land…

Follow up. Three weeks later.

"*The journey is awful. I have to think again about coming here. The train journey is long and uncomfortable.*" 'Leaking' what did you mean by 'leaking'?" She asks me as she sits.

I am confused. Had I said 'leaking'? Clearly I had, but meaning what?

"*You asked me to come back.*" She says "*and so I am here.*"

I wasn't expecting this. I wasn't aware of expecting anything, and certainly not this. Had I asked her to come back? I struggle to say some of this, remembering the importance of control for her.

"This is about who is in control?"

"I have got over that hump anyway, of having to control everything." She says

"I tend to do a gritty sticking with things rather than actually staying with experience. I run away from discomfort…… I have been getting rid of external discomforts too. I am allowing myself to be much more comfortable. Maybe coming here for supervision is too hard a journey; too far to come. I am getting in touch with the internal discomfort…I have been hiding my vulnerability from the judgemental homeopath in me, the one who has to be pure… You have to give up the myth, of being the all wise one, to be real."

"And real is…? "

"Real is hard."

On Reflection

In these fragments of conversation, at least two images are present: My sea metaphor is countered by Meg's land journey. Old colleagues that we are, we are still speaking different languages. We are 'strangers' or 'others' in a sense.

Who are our 'others?' Our 'not me' people?

Allopaths? War mongers? Racists? Meat eaters? Northerners? Southerners? Gays or straights? Children and babies? People who are old or dying? People with disability ? Our own diseases?

We all have them — how do you talk to them?

Take a few moments to brainstorm your 'others.'

Who are you in relation to each of them?

What is the space between you filled with?

Jot down some of the things that fill the space —

Lack of experience?

Ignorance?

Ideas about 'them'?

Fear?

Not all 'others' are groups of people we can identify as such.

Bring to mind someone apparently similar to you who feels 'other' in some way — you just can't get alongside them.

Jot down some of the things that fill the space between you.

Who are they for you?

What part of you that is hard to accept do they express?

Our familiars become 'others' from time to time — as in this supervision session.

Can you think of an example of a familiar becoming 'other'?

What happened?

Whose Story Is It Anyway?

The supervisory project is to notice what it is we each bring to the matter. I can see you more clearly in seeing what it is I bring.

I couldn't stay with Meg's land journey because I didn't notice that I was all at sea…

My image is all about fear of the depths we fathom in practice. Hers emphasise the discomfort of the journey, how hard it is. One will not do for the other. In referring only to my metaphor I author her story, twisting the tale to make sense to me rather than following hers. This parallels trying to fit a person to a remedy or other therapeutic model.

That our metaphors are at odds with each other 'echos' the content of the session. Meg was finding it hard to get alongside a group and just listen to what was there. Likewise, I was busily translating our session into a sea journey and not noticing she was bumping along on the road. I couldn't 'get alongside' her.

The content of the session included how hard it feels when feelings aren't shared. Our session paralleled this when I chose not to share my feelings of anxiety that I might not be able to help or the image of the sea that was arising in response.

When we're pre-occupied we're not present.

The Dynamics of Metaphor

'The boat capsizing in deep water' was my experience of this supervisory relationship at the time: What was happening and where were we going?

Would we be able to keep it afloat as a supervisory relationship, focussed on practice, or would we capsize into another focus, that of personal therapy?

The metaphor also asks the question: *"Is personal life sinking practice?"* The ethical issue arises, when are we fit to practice and when should we be resting in order to pay attention to what else is happening in our lives?

For the supervisee, her concerns were expressed in the *"gritty sticking with things."* She has come to supervision to *"explore the territory."* She feels uncomfortable in situations not grounded in feeling. Her response is to try to control what happens in those situations. The actual journey by train and bus to our appointment is becoming so uncomfortable that she is considering whether to carry on. Our sessions themselves become a metaphor for the state.

Metaphor Honours Difference

Our characteristic ways of experiencing are expressed often in metaphor,

"It's as if I'm midwife to the student I'm supervising while she is giving birth to her practice."

"It's like the supervisee needs me to be her idea of a perfect parent when I am aspiring to be 'good enough.'"

One metaphor will not do for another. Metaphor, as speech— or remedy, can be the moving line. It can also be a tyranny; crushing every other way of perceiving what the matter is. The story I tell here of Meg's supervision sessions is my own, hence the title. Here is a glimpse of her tale told to me in response to reading mine.

"I think what you were implying was that my emotions were leaking into my work. So for me 'leaking' was what I remembered because I didn't really understand it and it seemed to me it must be a clue for me to unlock something. Somehow though it became a 'sticking point' — it was something you shared with me, but not something you were able to use somehow the next time — so the metaphor left me a bit 'high and dry' if you like!!"

Raising and staying with metaphor, playing with metaphor is to follow the moving line.

The Moving Line

How are we moving? In what way? At what pace? Going towards what and away from what? What is it like?

A bumpy road?

A flame?

A river ?

A kite?

Dynamis is force in motion. A homeopathic movement; one that 'gets alongside,' is motion with the minimum force in the same direction.

When I want to force the pace of the supervision session and impose my sea and boat movement upon it, I am losing the pace and quality of the supervisee's journey. I am not yet 'getting alongside' her.

The task of the supervision is to *interrupt* the stuck narratives presented in seeing more of how it is. The sea metaphor, if used with consciousness, in a timely way and with permission, may come in here:

What if you weren't on a humpy bumpy land journey but were in the smooth and yielding sea, floating along?

Or *What could the opposite of a 'gritty sticking with it' be like?*

In creating this *aesthetic distance* from ourselves, in using metaphor we are encouraged to observe rather than be too attached to one idea of how it is. While one metaphor, or indeed one remedy, won't do for another, at the same time, considering another metaphor, or another remedy, reveals a new dimension to us.

Metaphorical expressions are a *minimum intervention,* an insight delivered in *potency* as it were. As such, even when only partially similar, they can be powerful agents of change. They can express the movement from rational reflection to dynamic practice where understanding is an immediate 'aha' moment rather than the rational explanation we give when we study our art and have to demonstrate to ourselves and others that we can think through a situation in a particular way — homeopathically, as an osteopath, in a Jungian way etc.

> "A writer is not interested in explaining reality; he's interested in capturing it." (Brendan Kennelly in Astley, 2002)

What is most helpful, supervisory and therapeutic? To explain or to capture what the matter is?

Poetry and the Dynamics of Dis-easing

> "Poems may well be the art of the unsayable.

Poems are an act of discovery.

A poem is unique to it's author.

Poems start in odd phrases, an image, a tune in the head, a deeply incoherent pain. How they develop is the poem." (Poetry Magic, 2003)

If we substitute the word 'dis-ease' for the word 'poem' we get this:

Dis-ease is the art of the unsayable.

Dis-ease is an act of discovery.

A dis-ease is unique to its author.

Dis-ease starts in odd phrases, as an image, a tune in the head, a deeply incoherent pain.

"…because a poem expresses the inexpressible. It desires to be spoken in the many languages of music, rhythm and beauty. It is so deep it cannot be told directly, it wants images, it wants metaphor." (Deena Metzger, 1992, p. 12)

When we are fit and well (or in love) we might express ourselves like this:

"I feel like a lark in the morning."

"I'm as happy as a pig in clover."

"I could spread my wings and do a thousand things"… Clichéd metaphors for well-being.

It is odd to say dis-ease is like a poem.

We say:

"I'm off colour. "I'm not myself." "I'm beside myself with worry or pain."

We are out of easy relationship with ourselves when we are ill. Illness expresses the inexpressible. It tells us we are not in right relationship.

We are *"devoured by it, drowning, exploding, the light has gone out, we are fading."*

Metaphors for disease. In this way it is like a poem. It isn't beautiful; it is suffering. Yet, if we can look it in the eye and see it for what it is, it has it's own rhythm, language, it's own beauty even. We don't see that because we are attached to it being different. I'd rather write a poem than become ill. Of course I would.

The Prejudice of Poets

"Many poets have theorized on the nature of their craft. Their aphorisms are very quotable, and often provide entry into new realms of thought, but they should be used with caution. Artists are notoriously partisan, and rarely paint the whole picture. To understand their pronouncements, you need first to love their work, be steeped in its vision, and then to measure their pronouncements against the larger conception of art that other work provides." (Poetry Magic, 2004)

The Healing Arts beg the question, *"Whose story are we telling?"* What is the evidence for this being the elemental story of the client/patient?

Observable signs and symptoms, recorded movements, patterns and shapes confirm or refine the stories we make about each other. Being present to the encounter so that we have full use of all our senses is the competence we need in order to check out the validity of the 'art work,' that is the 'case,' we are making.

It is our animal, instinctual, sensual, spontaneous selves we need. Our free selves, married to our more conscious, deliberating, aspiring natures. The marriage of Apollo with Dyonisus, the self we contact through our artistic and creative works; the letting go into the art and the taking stock, standing back and assessing in the light of experience, maps and models.

Supervision and Poetry

"Supervision is where we are open to those intuitive leaps of insight and empathy which are not easily accounted for in rational explanation." (Gaie Houston, 1990)

Brigid Proctor suggests:

"A group supervisor has to learn to trust his senses — to think in physical imagery — 'Who has the reins here?' 'Who is out in the cold?' ' Where have we got lost?' ' I was imagining a full-bodied bowl and suddenly it shattered.'" (2000)

This is the poet's art — to capture the essence. The aesthetic distancing of metaphor goes further than simile; either by saying that something is something else, for example, the state of this person with hay fever is a *Pulsatilla* flower, or by suggesting that something appears, sounds or behaves like something in a different element, for example,

"The sea that bares her bosom to the moon." (Wordsworth)

A simile is a comparison, as in *"He is like a bull in a china shop."* A homeopathic remedy is not a mere simile. It is analogous to the disease; it corresponds to the disease. In literary terms, it is a metaphor for the disease.

> "When we use simile we are describing one thing by comparing it to another. It is the safe route; reality is not shifted. Nothing happens when we say the bird's wings were blue as the sky. However, when we create a metaphor everything tilts; the bird made of sky…That is another matter." (Deena Metzger, 1992, p. 28.)

The centre of the case or the heart of the matter is often communicated in metaphor:

"I feel as if I am alone in the wilderness."

"The sensation is as if ants are crawling under my skin."

"There is an odd feeling, as if my face is covered in cobwebs."

Awareness of the tyranny of metaphor is the other side. In following one metaphor, telling one story, we are not then paying attention to another metaphor or to a different version of the story.

A checklist for writing a poem – and for finding out what the matter is.

Title. What name shall I give this?

Subject. What is the basic situation here?

Shape. What forms does it take, mentally, emotionally, physically, spiritually?

Tone. What attitude is taken towards the subject?

Word choice. How is the subject expressed verbally — and in the body language?

Personification. What is personified here? What is striking and persuasive? Where is the unity and power?

Metaphor and simile. How is the whole expressed in metaphor and simile?

Rhythm and metre. What is the natural and inevitable rhythm of the whole?

Overall impression. Standing back, what is the overall impression?

The healing arts are poetic in nature. For it is the poets' way; the way of Apollo and of Dionysus, to take us along the elusive paths of healing.

In getting more aware of the metaphors involved I can see our different tracks more clearly.

Vulnerability

With these supervision sessions with Meg I am reminded again of the power of vulnerability. (See The Transforming Triad in Chapter Four, 'Ain't Gonna Die for You.') The need to control outcomes fades away for Meg at the point she gets in touch with her own feelings. My need to control the session and apparently Meg's return to supervision, unconsciously parallels or 'echos' the state. This 'echo' is noticed on reflection only since I wasn't present to my own vulnerability during the session.

The Bigger Picture

These sessions remind me of the alchemical *Mappa Mundi*: Fire, Air, Water and Earth.

> "The Mappa Mundi was synthesised from traditional sources by the homeopath Joseph Reves of Israel and is referred to by him as 'The Circle.'
>
> 1. Fire, essentially heat, is an energy and without substance.
>
> 2. Air, being a vapour, is almost immaterial.
>
> 3. Water is fluid, not as yet formed and solid, as Earth.
>
> 4. Earth is dense and represents the ultimate stage in the process of solidification." (Misha Norland, *Mappa Mundi and the Dynamics of Change.*)

The four elements so described correspond to C.G.Jung's four psychological functions:

Fire — Intuition.

Air — Thinking.

Water — Feeling.

Earth — Sensing.

We *sense* something exists; we can touch it, smell it, see it and hear it. We can have a *felt-sense of* something; embody something; sense with the beginnings of movement.

We *feel* attracted to it and so *move* towards it or *feel* repelled by it and so move away from it.

We *think* about what it is. This includes reflecting upon it. We make rational sense of it. We judge something.

We *intuit* what it means; where it has come from and where it might go.

A metaphor can grasp the characteristic totality of this; the essence of a thing — what it is we sense, what we feel about it, think about it and intuit about it. What way it is moving and how we are moving in response to it.

For example, fire can warm, burn or consume. *"I am consumed by love."*

Air can be still, move gently as a breeze or blow as wind. *"I am blown about by circumstances. I can neither settle here nor there."*

Water flows, stagnates or gushes. *"If I start crying I will never stop. I will drown in my tears."*

Earth is solid, cracks open or erupts. *"If this carries on I will surely crack up."*

For our purposes, of 'getting alongside' each other in conversation, we can be guided by this ancient and Jungian mapping. It can raise awareness of the characteristic motion being expressed that may well be the clue to the dis-ease as well as to the mis-understandings we so readily achieve. Take these examples recorded in different supervision sessions:

"What's your sense of it?" (earth)

"I feel…" (water)

"Do you have a hunch what might happen? "(fire)

"I think…" (air)

"What do you feel about it?" (water)

"My sense is…" (earth)

"Do you have anything in mind?" (air)

"My intuition is…" (fire)

And noticing change in elements during a conversation

"What do you understand the matter to be in this case?" (air)

"I think he has never been well since losing his job. My feeling is that this is a loss of identity for him." (air to water)

"What's the feeling?"

"I just feel he was all tied up in that job…" (water — earth)

"Tied up?" (sense — earth)

From thought to feeling to sensation — tracking what the matter is.

Meg is emphasising her sense of the journey — it is uncomfortable. I am noticing the feelings – fear of their depth and cut off from feeling.

Awareness of the elements puts us in touch with movement — with motivation. Working at this level we are engaged with what really counts, not so much our comfort stories, the ones we tell ourselves to explain our lives, as much as our more elemental ones.

Exercising the elements

These exercises are designed to raise consciousness of our habitual ways of relating.

They may take a while to get the hang of. We can practice then since we're not 'perfects' after all. Each will take a few moments. A minimum intervention for the possibility of some surprising insights perhaps.

An exercise for the intuition

Sitting quietly. Relax. You may wish to tense and then relax your body, starting with your toes and working up in order to deepen the relaxation. (See Introduction, Activity: How do we listen to ourselves?)

Focus on your breath.

You are just letting your breath come and go. You are merely paying attention to it. Each time your attention wanders from your breath, and it will, you can just notice that and gently bring it back to focussing on your breath.

Now, allow a client to arise.

Many may clamour for attention.

Return to focussing on your breath.

Ask for one person only to come.

When one person has come and settled

Ask them what is the matter?

Allow them to answer.

If there is any struggle to think or answer for yourself, then return to focusing on your breath.

Let them answer.

What is the matter?

Allow the conversation to have you. Don't try to have the conversation.

Thank the person.

Return to the room.

Immediately write down what you have received verbatim, without judgement or editing.

How does the impression you have received through the meditation compare with your understanding of the person?

What have you learned?

A thinking exercise.

More often than not thoughts think us. How much do we think through something? Thoughts occur. Actively thinking, like actively listening, is an intentional act. An act of the will that is maintained only with practice.

Begin by relaxing as before.

Focus on the breath (see exercise for the intuition)

Intend to think about something, preferably something simple or downright silly, for five minutes, and say for example;

"I intend to think about what I will have for my dinner."

Think about your dinner. What you will have. How you will have it. How it will be procured. How it will be prepared or cooked. When, where and with whom you will eat it.

Each time your thoughts stray from the subject of your dinner, make a mental note that they have and return to thinking about your dinner.

What happened?

Have you thought about your dinner?

What else happened?

Does your thinking come with images, words, insights, intuitions, senses, feelings?

Were there thoughts you could scarcely put a name to?(*Felt sense*)

Did you think about your dinner in new ways?

Has any real decision or action come out of thinking about your dinner?

An exercise for the senses.

Sitting quietly, relaxing and focusing on the breath as before, call up a patient/ client.

Can you see them before you?

What do they look like?

Do they give you permission to explore?

If so;

First, roll them into a ball and pop them into your mouth.

What do they taste like?

Next, hold them up to your ear.

What sound do they make?

Bring them to your nose.

What do they smell like?

Now, hold them in front of you and stroke.

What do they feel like?

Thank the person.

Return to the room.

Do it without aforethought.

Write down the impressions you have received.

Do they contribute to your perception of what ails the person or your obstacle to perceiving them?

What is your reaction to them during the exercise?

What does this reveal?

And one for feelings.

You are looking forward to something. It depends on someone else. Maybe appreciation for something you have done, or the happiness you will bring to someone. In the event, they don't respond as you hope and expect.

Can you find an example of this?

What happened?

What feelings do you run through before coming to accept that it isn't as you hoped or expected?

Is there an example of not yet coming to accept what happened?

What is the feeling?

What is left in the strainer?

Is this what the matter is?

What feelings are in the gap between what we expect and what happens?

Raising Metaphor

Metaphor is a powerful tool for capturing the elemental state. Metaphors, like homeopathically prescribed potentised remedies, can take us straight to the heart of the matter. They can move us. They can also stop us in our tracks.

The questions raised include:

Whose story is it anyway?

What are we co-creating here?

What is the story we are co-creating telling us about what the matter is?

How are we moving and in what direction?

These questions speak of the quiet adventure of healing relationship; the weaving of our tales; the reinvention of our stories — the epic journeys we make together.

The last story takes us on such a journey. We lose the way and find it again in tracking the path home, as a dog does, as a wolf does, as our wild and instinctual, civilised and soulful selves do.

Mappa Mundi and Supervision Styles

Supervision is enthusiastic, spontaneous; using
creative techniques, visualisations, play and drama.
Interest in relationships, transference, etc.
Supervisor can be flexible, dynamic, catalytic,
uses empathic responses, and personal awareness.
Uses journal as scrapbook, or sketchbook.

But can be too creative with the facts,
can jump to conclusions; forget to contract;
lack solid advice and direction for the supervisee.

Supervision is organized, systematic, prepared in advance; careful contracting and a structured session. Supervisor wants to know facts and details of appointments; interest in content, uses body language to mirror interest and summarizes well. Uses journal to record.

But can be dry, flat, heavy, stuck to routines, not creative, unable to help with stuck cases.

Fire
Intuition

Earth
Sensation

Water
Feeling

Air
Thinking

Supervision is fluid, flexible, with a free-flow session, allowing anything to come up and encouraging interaction. Lots of empathy and support. Supervisor considers own feelings/ process during the session, uses parallel process. Uses journal to write about feelings.

But can be so empathic and supportive, there is no challenge. Boundaries can get lost, contract forgotten.

Supervision is intellectual, informative,
didactic; with references to books, theoretical
models; sound advice and considered contracting.
Supervisor interested in analyzing, diagnosing
interactions (transference, parallel process);
uses challenges and summarizes well.
Uses journal to analyze, and discuss theory.

But can get too interested in teaching,
become so wordy or theoretical that the supervisee
doesn't understand; or doesn't give them the
opportunity to think for themselves.

© Jane Wood 2001

THE DOG'S STORY

The Mad Dog and the Wolf: Bringing Home the Wild and the Civilised

CHAPTER SEVEN

The most effective supervision is a mercurial thing (see Chapter Four, 'Ain't Gonna Die for You'). It is hard to get a hold of, difficult to say what is happening or why. In bringing together the scattered parts of the story, supervision as a quality of looking, attempts to see where we are without fear or favour.

This chapter follows the dog's story as it weaves its way through relationship, dream, conversation, myth and proving. In following the thread where will it take us?

The chapter is also bringing together the different strands of the book. What have we gathered in of the scattered stories and how will the journeying continue?

The story begins with a dream.

"I am in my campervan with the side door slid nearly shut. My dog, who had been inside, somehow escapes through a crack in the door. She bounds away over a meadow lit up by the late afternoon sun, shadows lengthening away at the tree line. I am confident she will return to me in her own sweet time. Then, as a dark cloud passes over the van, blotting out the light, I am afraid. Afraid she might get lost and not come home, or worse, that she might worry or even kill a lamb while she is out."

I wake up, write the dream down and later share it with a friend, who in her work as a therapist, is in daily conversation with dreams. (Brita Andrews, 1998)

This is how we talk. The dog is a civilised wolf escaping from the confines of the campervan, itself an image of travelling into the wilds — albeit with a house in tow. Dual nature; the wild, instinctual, animal self and the more civilised, conscious being are both here again.

The camper van and the dog seem to connect the two worlds in their semi-wildness. The door separating the two is not completely closed. Love of the dog's freedom and fear of the wolf's wildness is here.

The dream speaks directly to my experience of writing this book. I have a task; to convey something of the nature of the homeopathic and supervisory project. If I let the book go its own wild way, where will it end up? It might kill the project. I have to keep it on a leash, keep reining it in. At the same time, if I don't let it go, it can't convey something of the essence of the thing...

The Dog's Story

The ancients knew dog's milk to be a powerful remedy and antidote to many deadly poisons. (Tyler, 1952) I was also working at the time of the dream with a man recovering from alcohol dependence and its poisoning effects. Now ' dry,' Phil inhabits a world of self disgust, fear and anger. Being with him brings to mind walking warily along a precarious icy ledge, half way up a mountain and in a gale. I am expecting him to fall at any moment. He surprises me with his tenacity; looking down time and again into the abyss, terrified of falling, holding on at times by his fingertips.

(To be homeopathic, we walk the way of the other and in "their territory" (Norland, see Facilitation as Story-telling in Chapter Four, 'Ain't Gonna Die for You.')

Two striking features lead to the remedy *Lac Caninum* (dog's milk) for Phil. He feels such disgust for himself that he *"could not bear to be in his body "*he says, and, related to this, that *"Everyone was right to look down upon him."* He reacts strongly to the remedy, needing to be 'held' through the process. I need in turn to keep a hold. I ask myself

"Who am I for him?"

The essence of the dog's milk *proving* is expressed by the phrase *"Believing oneself held in contempt."* Certainly if ever there was a man in need of unconditional loving he is it.

He says

"I must always remember, on a daily basis, how lucky I am and how bad I've been....

Addiction is a dog at my heels...

My behaviour is so low

You walk in dark places if you go with me

I need to be led."

The tamed wolf is a creature of shame; licking instead of biting the hand that feeds. He is also the conduit — between wild and tame — the dog can turn after all.

Yearning to belong. Anxious he will never belong, will never tame the wildness. Unable to express the conflict between primal and civilised self. At a physical level, *Lac caninum* shows this in wandering, undecided pains, from side to side, typically in the throat. Literally 'going for their throats.'

As with the D.T.s, they can see snakes and in fear and revulsion suffer sudden attacks of violent rage. They know there is something wrong with them and they can't contact it; the source of healing, the wildness.

In mythology the dog is the guardian at the gates of the underworld. The dog accompanies the fool on her journey into the unknown. The dog too is the magic animal. He brings back what has been forgotten and must now be re-membered.

There was no way I could step out onto that ledge with Phil without the help of animal nature. There was no way I could track this patient without stepping out there.

I had my ropes and ice picks sure; the formal space of the consultation - and the remedy; the echo answering his call. I could hold on. I could cut the rope too and let him fall if needs be to save my skin. (I may be a fool but I'm not that foolish.) One reason as a homeopath to work with others — to be in supervision — someone to hold my rope while I'm holding his. The addicted patient being with a recovering addict as mentor also supports the therapeutic process in that I am freed from following every stumble to look back at the way we have come and on to the way ahead. Up to this point we are safe enough. It is a dog's tale — no wild wolf here. We are hanging onto the ledge; the abyss far below. And when we fall?

I am reminded that *Hermes,* Greek mercury (see Chapter Four, 'Ain't Gonna Die for You') was previously associated with roadways and boundaries among other things. Getting lost, slipping into the experience, 'bearing' the dis-ease (see Chapter Three, 'Cheetah') requires the 'safe enough' and 'risky enough' presence of formal space: There is a distinction to be made after all between everyday conversation and the highly charged activity of story telling and active listening. (See Chapter Two, 'Let's Go Fly a Kite.') Ariadne, Cretan Moon Goddess, consort of Dyonisus and maiden who helps Theseus through the Labrynth with her thread, also comes to mind here as a symbol of the process of 'getting lost' in the story and then finding the way back home.

The tale continues

"Manawee wishes to marry. The father of the twins he courts tells him he has first to guess their names. This he fails to do. His dog runs back to the twin's hut and listens to their conversation. They talk to each other using their names. He starts on his way back to his master to tell him the names. On the way he is distracted by a large meaty bone a lion had left. He smells it and without another thought, leaves off his journey to lick all the flavour from the bone. He forgets his task and the names of the women. Again and again he returns to the hut and again and again he is distracted and forgets his task and the names. It is only in the nick of time, as the sisters are about to wed, that the little dog keeps to his resolution and goes straight away to his master and reveals the names. He has to ignore tempting scents and tracks. He survives a terrible fight with a stranger who wounds him. He keeps to his path. The man on hearing the names, bathes the dog's wounds and hoists him onto his shoulders. He then runs to the sisters and finds them dressed ready to journey with him as his brides. They all live happily ever after, the man, the twins and the dog."(Clarissa Pinkola-Estes, 1992 paraphrased)

The Task

The dog is the magician who can pass through the crack in the door in search of knowledge. What is the knowledge to be brought back in each case? The task of the dog, the wild to civilised animal, is to bring it back. A part of each of us is open to receiving knowledge, be it just a crack, the magician will pass through.

Dual nature; civilised and wild, is married in this story in the body of the twins, but only after the task is completed, the knowledge gained, the names remembered.

It is the task that is important. It is that in the end that moves us along, keeping us to the path: What is the task in the story? To remember the name.

What is the patient in my story trying to name?

What is the name of the remedy that answers?

That is my task, to follow the path without distraction.

Feelings and sensations can be temptations and distractions along the way. We have to get right down to it, like the dog, in the nick of time fighting for it, as if our lives depend upon it, and then we remember and act on what we know.

What is the name of the dis-ease?

What is its action?

What is its path?

Keep to the path.

Remember the name.

Carrion eaters including the dog are universally associated with funerary customs and passage to the underworld.

Hecate, the death goddess, had her gates guarded by the three headed hound, Cerberus. The dog in these terms is a symbol of journeying into unconsciousness; both conduit and guardian.

My dream echos through the work with Phil. It gives me confidence to go on, trusting to his unfolding story. If the dog can hold the door open to the wild, even a crack, then more than recovery from alcoholism is possible; taming the beast. Recovering his own wild nature is possible. Healing disgust for who he is becomes possible.

What is the knowledge to be fetched back from the wild?

What is it we need to know?

What have we buried for shame?

Both the dream and the fable of Manawee are relevant to our task of healing relationship in that they remind us to hold the connection between the rational technical side and letting go into the unknown to learn anew.

Apollo and Dionysus are with us at every twist in the tale.

The next day after my dream, while out walking in the countryside, I stopped to watch a herd of cattle. Two large cows, full udders swinging, were going at it head to head, pushing and shoving each other, slipping and staggering about in the mire and pats. Other cows were moving in on them, nuzzling the rear of one and shoving at the side of the other. A little way off, one cow mounted another. They weren't mad cows but simply expressing their wildish natures. So much for polarising the herd (or flock) and the pack — the one will get into the other!

Re-membering

We get lost in our dreams, intuitions, *felt-senses*, metaphors — and find the way back out again to a more conscious, rational understanding. We are like Hansel and Gretel, exiled in the wood, laying a trail of crumbs; or like Ariadne laying down thread. As in fairy tales and myths, sometimes the journey is longer, harder, requires more craft and endurance than we are prepared for and even then we are asked to go on again.

We need all the clues we can find on such a journey; both to go on as far as we need to go and to re-member the way home.

Re-membering Dreams

Keeping a dream diary.

Intention is everything. In intending to make our dreams the subject of inquiry and practicing that inquiry daily, we are most of the way there. We begin to re-member our dreams and experience the correspondences, synchronicities and serendipities familiar to the explorer in myths and fairy tales.

In sleeping by ourselves, as some animals and children do, we sleep with the intention of following our dreams. In sleeping and waking to our own rhythm, rather than being woken by an external alarm or interruption, we give ourselves the optimum conditions for taking notice of our dreams.

As you dream and wake, during the night as well as in the morning, take a moment to write down or draw, or make in some moulding material, what you remember. Then like good bread, let it rise, revealing over time, something of it's nature to you.

Meeting in a group to share dreams, in a way of group supervising each other, can greatly add to the richness and transformative power of your dream world.

Working with dreams with other people, letting the meaning unfold within the story world of the other person, rather than imposing any of our own interpretations, can go a long way to reveal the elemental story, and in a way that is empowering to the other.

Active listening, including being aware of the bigger stories the dream may be referring to, helps with making meaning. It is not to be interpretative and imposing a story so much as tentatively asking in the spirit of inquiry. "What is it like? This? Or this?"

(See Robin Shohet, 1985 for an inspirational resource and guide to sharing your dreams.)

In remembering and writing down dreams, and particularly in sharing them with inquiring others, as well as with our own inquiring self, we find sustenance for our journey.

In remembering and writing down fairy tales, myths and legends we have archetypal stories in which to explore our own heroic journeying. Angela Carter (1990) refers to this property of fairy tales as 'public dreaming.'

Journey

The homeopathic way is to journey in the direction already taken: to get alongside. The noticing is that feelings very often lead the way into the journey and that feelings too can just as often lose us the way; distracting, side-tracking, throwing us off the scent as in the story of Manawee.

I use the term *felt-sense* to communicate the idea of feelings barely articulated, feelings that are sensed by the body rather than named as such. They aren't yet attached to some *comfort story*. These take us to the more *e-motional* feelings — those connected to movement — and so down to the *elemental story*.

E-motion

Amoebas continually change shape in response to more or less favourable conditions. Immobile sea sponges produce unpleasant tasting chemicals to ward off prey. The sea anemone, a flower like animal, opens and closes it's tentacles, and on being touched, shoots out stinging cells.

These simple creatures are showing what I am calling, in a rather over simplified way, *e-motion*. They are reacting, automatically, to the presence of threat or prey.

In evolutionary terms, e-motion comes before conscious feeling. It is an instinctive response, involving an automatic physical reaction. (For a proper discussion of the neurobiology of emotion and feeling see to the work of Antonio Damasio, 2003, Chapter Two and to his categorisation of emotion for the purposes of inquiry.)

> "The single word homeostasis is convenient shorthand for the ensemble of regulations and the resulting state of regulated life." (Damasio, 2003)

This is why the cravings and aversions take such high prominence in a homeopath's case recording; because all our various movements are designed, automatically, to bring us to equilibrium. This is mirrored in our appetites: We go about it in an odd way very often; it doesn't look like any straight forward motion, but that's us getting in the way of ourselves again isn't it?

"I want you to love me and so I will say horrible things to you and push you away."(Ignatia in love)

"I want to love and so I will choose a completely unsuitable and unavailable person to worship."(Natrum Muriaticum in love)

It does make sense of a kind once the full story is known…

Exercising the e-motions.

What motivates you? Moves you?

When push comes to shove, what gets you up in the morning?

What do you love?

The miracle question.

Relax.

Focus on the breath. (see to introduction exercises)

If you went to sleep tonight, and on waking tomorrow, the thing you love most to happen had been miraculously accomplished, what would it look like?

What would you do in response?

What changes would you make?

What would your world look like?

Where would you be in it?

Write it all down. Just as it comes, without pausing, judging or editing.

What one thing could you do, step you could take, today, to bring you nearer to the world you love?

Feeling

Feelings come and go. We can change them. They are our own, individual and private story. We make and re-make that constantly. The parts that settle become our *comfort (or discomfort) stories;* the sense and nonsense we make of our lives. Tell or hear our stories differently and the feelings shifts; the comfort story is *interrupted.*

In telling our story to an *active listener* we can feel significantly better. (See Chapter One, 'What Is the Matter?') For a time that is. Feelings have been aired, shared, released, reframed and re-storyed. Sometimes this enables us to make actual changes, if the more *elemental story,* that which speaks to our more primal motivations, is contacted. Often it isn't. The motive force, the *e-motion,* has not yet been engaged.

Damasio:

> "The 'primary' (or basic) emotions are easier to define [than 'background' emotions — see to Damasio] because there is an established tradition of lumping certain prominent emotions in this group. The frequent listing includes fear, anger, disgust, surprise, sadness and happiness — the emotions that first come to mind whenever the term emotion is invoked. There are good reasons for this centrality. These emotions are easily identifiable in human beings across several cultures and in *non human species as well*."(Stress is mine.) (2003, p. 44)

'E-motion,' core motivation, is 'non human specific.' (Sankaran, 2002) This is the level we are getting down to when we are looking at healing and dis-easing. When we are in touch with how our body moves and changes, expresses disturbance, in sensations and function, we are connecting with the force for change. (See also Sherr, 2002 'The verb')

I'm adopting the term *e-motion* simply to express *felt-sense* with enough force behind it to move us. It is reaction more than response. Feeling and e-motion are more properly indistinctly separated along a continuum between automatic, primal survival reactions and highly conscious, private, finely tuned sensitivity. We track through feelings very often, and sometimes we are waylaid there, like the dog in the tale Manawee, or else we can't get a toehold in the first place, like Phil who has forgotten himself in addiction, and in either case, we lose our way.

Addiction Is a Case in Point

Working with addictive tendencies emphasises that talk and comprehension are not enough. E-motions that literally move us to tears, shake us with fear or curl us up in mortification are required. We are looking for the movement. Feelings are not enough.

When Phil is suffering withdrawal from addiction, his *felt-sense* of being precarious, needing to hold on, to do anything, drink himself to death rather than fall, took us to the movement of the remedy most homeopathic to him at that time, or so it seemed to me: Descent into self loathing, disgust and absolute contempt: Falling and fear of falling.

Lac Caninum has a sense of floating in air. The body is a loathsome, dirty thing to inhabit.

The Journey of Twelve Steps

The '12 steps programme' for recovery from addiction, can be seen in the light of heroic tasks needing to be undertaken before a cycle of an inner transforming journey is completed. The programme involves being sponsored by a guide or mentor who, as in archetypal stories, has gone before on the journey, and can therefore now offer protection along the way. To change the fixed pattern of addiction we *get alongside* the other, walk the way with them. We *do* something; go out on a limb. It is easy to lose our way without a guide; to be waylaid, like Manawee, by oral satisfactions that distract us from our task; both filling us up and leaving us empty.

Phil is a good patient, a good twelve stepper. He stays with the programme. He stays with the remedy. Like a tame dog, he doesn't bite the hand that feeds him. He walks along the ledge, holding on by his finger tips at times, not looking down into the abyss. What is down there Phil?

In order to follow patients recovering from addiction, I need my guides; both the civilising maps and wild instinctual nature expressed in dreams and images. The dog expresses for me both wild nature and the way back home. Dogs are loyal pet animals as well as their wolvish selves. They guard the door between the known and risky, unknown, shadow worlds. I am stepping into the scary world of the recovering addict. In getting alongside my patient I am very glad to have the dog alongside me.

Hands

Another patient, a young teenager born to a woman using heroin, had the peculiar symptom of not being able to stand her fingers to touch each other. She had very low self esteem, anorexia and a 'hang dog' expression. She recovered her spirits with *Lac Caninum* and went on to express herself as a white faced, black clothed gothic beauty. She was 'wolf whistled' wherever she went.

Rajan Sankaran (2002) in referring to 'non human specific' signs and symptoms, says these always involve movement. He focuses on the hand gesture in homeopathic consultation. The hands have an especial importance in world mythology:

> [Hands are] "those parts of our bodies that are like two small human beings in and of themselves. In olden times, the fingers were likened to legs and arms and the wrist joint to the head. Those beings can dance, they can sing." (Clarissa Pinkola Estes, 1992, p. 408)

And from the same book, discussing the meanings of the myth of the Handless Maiden. (The devil has ordered the father to cut off the hands of his daughter.)

> "We can understand the removal of psychic hands in much the same way the symbol was understood by the ancients. In Asia, the celestial axe was used to cut one away from the unillumined self. ... [By] cutting off her hands, the father deepens the descent, hastens the 'disolutio', the difficult loss of all one's dearest values, which means everything, the loss of vantage point, the loss of horizon lines, the loss of one's bearings about what one believes and for what reason.... When we say a woman's hands are cut off, we mean she is bound away from self-comfort, from immediate self-healing, so very helpless to do anything except follow the age-old path."

The hands express the *elemental story*, the one telling what it is drives us. Phil in recovery clings onto the path with his hands to prevent the fall. In the case of the young Goth girl, *Lac Caninum* cannot bear the fingers of the hands to touch each other. They are the 'little body' she cannot bear to inhabit.

Dis-easing is pointed up to us in signs, symptoms and body language, gesture and posture. It is also pointed up in dreams, fantasies and illusions, cravings and aversions. Fine feeling helps us differentiate, characterise, get alongside, empathise. To play on the surface though is not enough. We have to get on down into the depths, go fishing for pearls.

At every point in writing this book when I have fallen deeper into a story and have felt lost and uncertain about where it might be leading me and whether I should go on, I have dreamed something of the way. While considering the handless maiden and it's relevance to Sankaran's noticing of the hands, I dreamed that I not only had my hands cut off but my head too.

Again in conversation, the paralysing head of Medusa, who turns all to stone, came to mind.

Medusa is decapitated by Perseus as he rescues Andromeda who is chained to a rock. Beheading is associated with setting free. In one writing of the story, Medusa's head drips blood through the sack it is being carried in. As each drop falls, a flying horse rises. (Alix Pirani, 1988)

The dream and this reading of it reminds me of the requirement to follow this book as journey, not knowing in advance where it might lead but letting it take it's own flight.

This play between the 'expert' who knows in advance and 'the fool' who is willing to find out, is another way of expressing the task of healing relationship; to move back and forth between less conscious and more rational understanding.

Fool — Another Face of Shame

A common part of the practitioner-client story, is that the practitioner is wiser than the client. She is supposed to know what the matter is. If not, why come?

"It is the wise part of me I take into practice. I leave the foolish part, the lazy, the mean spirited, the doubtful, the selfish at home."

(*"Oh thank-you"* say the partners and the children and the friends.)

And is she wise about her clients?

She has some stories, some maps and some guides.

Does she know where the patient is in relation to these? Whether new maps are needed? Revisions of existing maps? A story to be told that is new to her?

Who will best find out about this patient? Is it the wise one or the fool? And what of the wisdom of the patient?

These foolish things remind me of you…

What was the most foolish thing you ever did? Write it down. Oh go on. You can tear it up afterwards. What happened? It was foolish because?

Now, turn it around.

What were you vulnerable to?

What was powerful about this experience?

What is it now that you take this time to reflect on it?

What if you turned it around and said it was a wise thing?

What could be wise about it?

How could it serve you, or what could you understand about yourself, your talents, if you weren't so busy naming it as a foolish thing?

What part of you do you leave at home in order to practice? A sense of mischief? Irreverence? Selfishness? Laziness? Stupidity? What are you ashamed of?

Consider, what characteristics would you be mortified to be found to have by a patient or client and colleague?

Are they the same or different for patients as for colleagues? And for a partner or friend?

What must you not be in practice?

Now, what virtues might these banned characteristics have? How do they serve you? How could they serve your ease and therefore your effectiveness in practice?

Tarot images of the fool always contain a dog.

Expert

An *expert* knows what she needs to know; expert routines. She has seen it all before. If she comes across something she hasn't seen before, she first tries to fit it into known categories. If it doesn't fit, she may invent new ones. These are usually named after her (read 'him').

Expert routines are very useful. For example at an emergency: Knowledge, practice, experience, confidence and competence are all needed. Something else too; the ability to think on our feet, to be *reflective in action:* (Schon, 1983) The willingness both to abandon and to remember all previous expertise in order to be in the moment; to make compassionate and creative decisions, and fast, using all previous expertise while inventing anew on the spot. Being in touch with instinct, art and craft, risk taking and courage all tell here. In other words being *present.* This is a dynamic; a vital practice.

Picture a roadside emergency:

A cyclist is lying unconscious, her bicycle, front wheel buckled, the other spinning wildly, is flung down beside her. The driver of a stopped car, doors hanging open, is sitting on the kerb, head in hands. His passengers are straying across the road like so many chickens.

Someone calm needs to take over. Someone who knows what to do first and to whom: Delegating, organising, re-creating order. We can be sure the bicycle will be the last to be righted when an expert in routine *and* reflection is in charge.

Mostly we are not responding to emergencies. Lives generally unravel much more quietly. We barely notice if at all where it all started to go wrong.

"Where did it start? Do you remember a time when you felt well?"

We may ask. It is hard to remember. Dis-easing has no clear beginnings.

We can have the illusion that we can cure named diseases, the ultimates of dis-ease, we can't. We are palliating symptoms. We can play for time though. We can bring our cunning to outwit the disease, to give more time to restore order. We can use our craftiness too, to palliate suffering. In order to do so we needs be expert in our own healing modality. In fact we had better learn our art well, for we are none of us experts in the life of another.

And in our own lives? Now that is another matter. If I learn more about myself, am more present to myself, become more attuned to myself in my surroundings, can I think and act on my feet more easily? Am I better placed to find out about another? To make a 'creative adjustment' as the Gestalt therapist might put it? Hardly an expert in myself — it never becomes routine — there is always the surprise — but being more knowledgeable about myself gives me a firm basis from which to respond in the moment.

In what ways are you an expert? What are you expert in? When is being expert helpful and when a hindrance to your practice? If a respected friend and colleague were to hear you being 'expert' would you be proud or mortified by that?

Phil is an 'expert' in addiction. He knows all the wily ways of it. He's nobody's fool when it comes to that. He knows what to do to beat it. To be good. To be recovered. To be a model ex-addict. Only a fool would look down into the abyss. Why so angry Phil? Punch the wall. Don't dare have a relationship. Yearn for family life, to belong. Cower from it as from poisoned wine.

The Wolf and the Mad Dog

The image that arose for me in relationship to Phil, was a landscape in which the wolf would have been very much at home. A bleak and snowy terrain hiding warm earth, fireside and friendship. The wolf's story is quite different from the dog's. The dog knows there is something wrong with him. He has lost his way. The focus is on the body. The dog is not aware of his 'psychic captivity' in the way the wolf is. The wolf however knows there is something wrong with the world — it has lost its way. (Assilem, 1997, *Lac Lupinum*)

Witness the ambivalent relationship to wolves in the new wave of persecution of them in the wilderness areas of the USA. They have been re-introduced there since the mid 1990s, dividing the communities between those who welcome their wildness and others who fear it and work for their extinction.

Phil continued to recover from his addiction to alcohol, uncovering as he did a terrible rage. This both relieved and terrified him. The remedy *Lyssin* (saliva of rabid dog)came in here as he railed against those he fancied himself dependent upon — including me: Missed appointments, turning up late, catatonic silences all characterised this period. It would be so easy to lose the way at this point. Holding the dog before us kept us on track. We literally nosed along. No longer the beaten and tame dog but the mad and maddened creature, caught by the tail and spun by the devil. Wild nature through a toxic screen. Not for Phil the lone grandeur of the howling wolf. He did stay the course. He did remember his name. He fell down into the abyss and returned to tell his tale.

He went on to tell his tale to young addicted men in prison. He turned it around he told them: Victim to vulnerable. Persecuted to potent. Rescued to reflective. (See Chapter Three, 'Cheetah.') Hats off to Phil. A dogged traveller if ever there was one.

Inquiring Within

To work at the level of what I am calling here *e-motion* requires of us a willingness to get interested. To get really interested — in ourselves as well as the other. To 'wake up' to our wild and instinctual, artistic and poetic, risk taking and courageous selves as well as to our more rational — technical knowings. To do this we meet all our devils along the way; our shame and fear and prejudice as well as what we value, believe in and espouse.

But why inquire into ourselves and not just the person who has come to see us?

Because we only know others at the level we know ourselves?

Because if we are willing to know the wild, the instinctual, the poet and the *fool* we might inspire others to some measure of self acceptance?

Because it is hard to deify a *fool*?

Because we don't have to carry the false burden of wise healer?

Because we can enjoy the freedom of the court jester to say what he means?

Because the deeper we go the stronger are the connections to others?

Because by being with you, I find myself and in being with myself I find you?

All good questions to reason with.

Vital Practice

We know what the matter is really but sometimes it is very hard to witness. We prefer to tell all sorts of stories instead,

"It's because of this and that."

"It happened so long ago and can't be changed now."

"I can't change it without them doing something first"

"I don't remember."

"It isn't me it's this wretched illness…"

We come to the healing arts for witness; to stay on track, to retrace our steps, to re-connect with our e-motions, to hear our elemental stories in the echo between story teller and active listener…

I am a beaten dog
Who has forgotten the wolf
Who has lost his way
Who is holding on
Who is falling away
What is my name?

The Three Questions

We came in with three questions. They have weaved their way through our stories.

1. Are some people healers and others not?

There are no healers, only healing relationship, our stories have replied. There is only the way we relate to the healing archetype; to the dissolving of separation through compassionate inquiry:

"How is it for you?"

There is only the moment. What is the quality of my presence in this moment? How does my presence contribute to healing or not?

2. Do we think we can heal anyone but ourselves?

"Healing is a self healing project," comes the reply.

How do I move in relationship to myself? To you? To the world around me?

With self knowledge comes knowledge of the other
Comes union with the other
Comes Healing.

3. What is the difference between healing and curing diseases?

Diseases are their own story we are told. They come with their own life force.We listen to the story of disease written in signs, symptoms and motions. We listen with respect, with unconditional acceptance.

Where are we at ease? Where do we feel the separation between 'I' and 'my?' What is the nature of the dis-ease?

What is it like? What in the world is it like?

A barking dog?
A howling wolf?
A high kite flying on a wild and windy day?

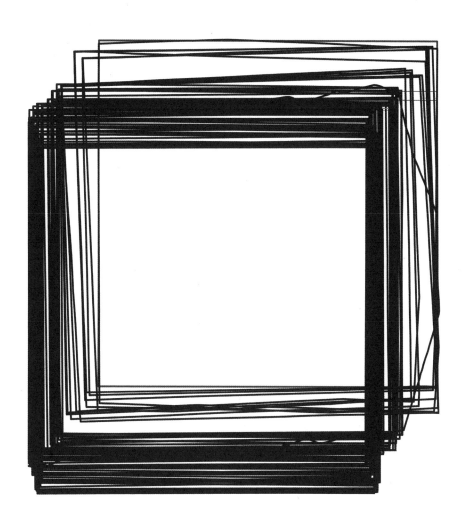

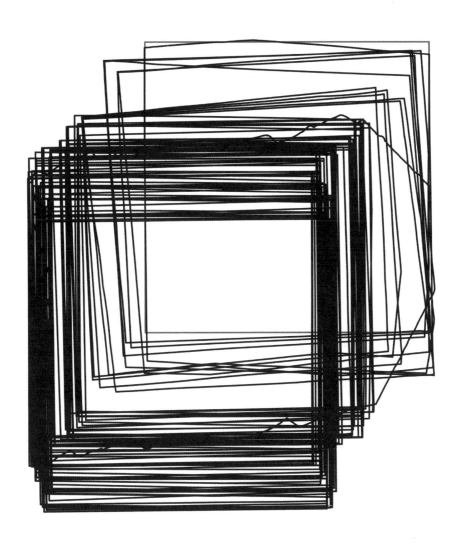

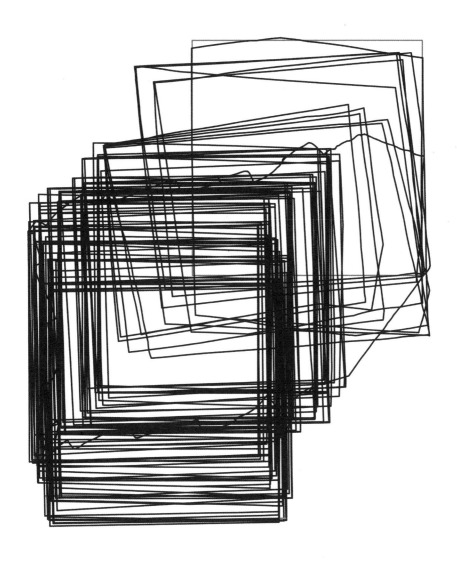

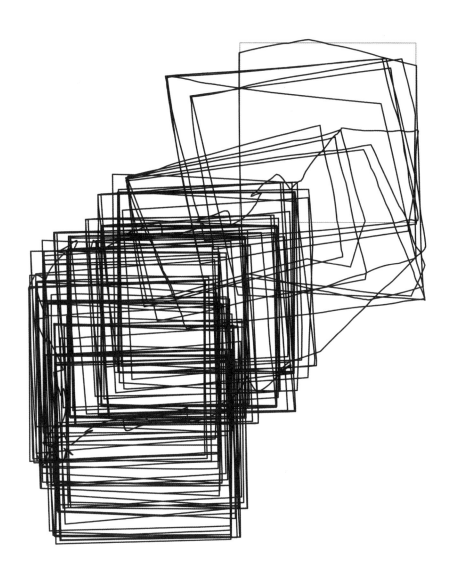

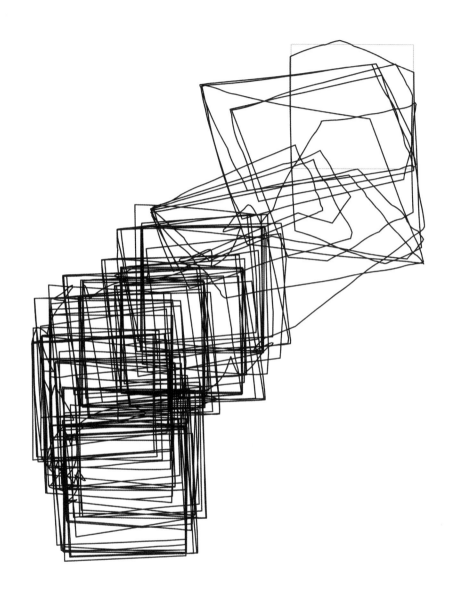

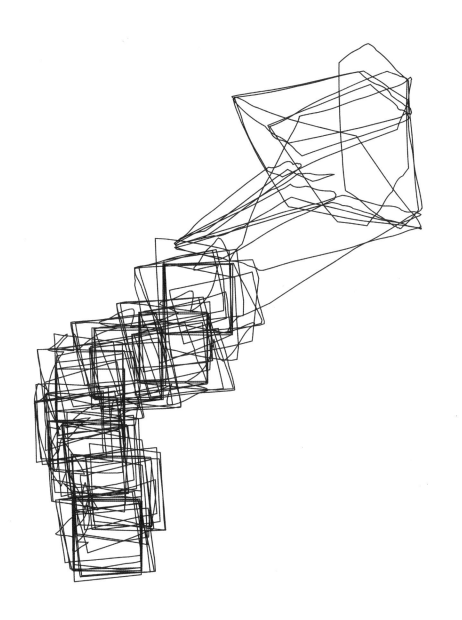

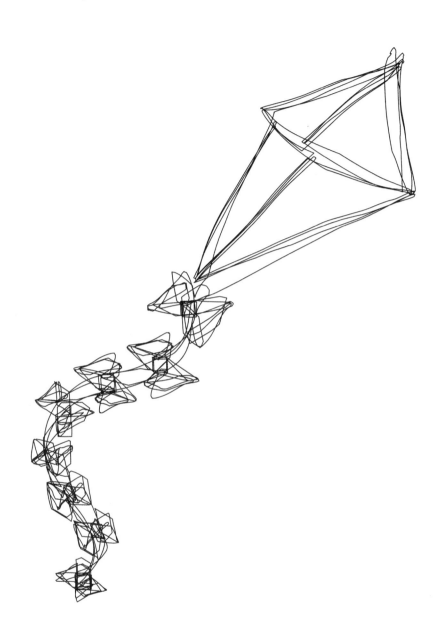

VITAL KIT

Introduction

The stories in this collection show something of the nature of homeopathic relationship and specifically a homeopathic approach to supervision. They focus on supervision as a quality of looking, with acceptance, at what is present here, and here and here.

'Vital Kit' supplies some short guides to the practice in a supervisory context, to be added to those followed on the way through the book.

Vital Kit is divided into three related sections:

- Making and Maintaining Working Relationship
- Triading, Working in Threes
- Contexts

Whether the relationship is to ourselves as in self supervising or self healing, or is one-to-one, in a group, with a client present or not, or on the phone and by e-mail, making and maintaining a working relationship appropriate to the task is both a necessary and an ethical practice. We are in effect telling ourselves and each other why we are here, what our expectations are and what competence we are bringing. In the telling we get clearer about how willing and able we are to revise, change or develop what we do.

'Making and Maintaining Working Relationship' introduces 'C.E.P.— Competence, Expectations and Process' as a guide to working relationship. 'Contracting' explores the boundaries and flexibility required both to clarify intention and to respond to each unique situation.

Three are always present. Whether or not we formally 'triad' in group supervision; client, practitioner and observing self are always there. Further, from a systemic perspective, there are many triads present. (See A Systemic Perspective in Chapter Three, 'Cheetah.')

The community in which we live and practice, the therapeutic interventions we make, the competence, expectations, prejudices, maps and models we bring, the stories we make, all these together make with us a network of triads. Some examples: Patient, Homeopath and Remedy; Client, Therapist and Therapeutic model; Teller, Listener and Story.

Practicing triading in a formal space, in order to inquire into the dynamics of practice, is a vital part of the Kit.

'Guides for Triading' include 'Setting The Scene,' 'Functions of Triading,' 'Facilitating Practice in Threes,' 'Roles and Tasks,' 'Whole Group Triading,' 'The Art of Feedback' and 'Voices' in which the archetypal characters we bring to practice are explored.

The purpose of guides to supervision in different contexts is to wake us up to the unique possibilities inherent in each situation. Every apparent limitation in so-called 'bare-foot' situations, for example only being able to have phone or email contact, or not sharing a common verbal first language, is explored for its characteristic expression. We can learn afresh precisely because we aren't entirely in our comfort zones.

'Contexts' develops guidance to 'Self,' 'Live Group Clinical,' and 'E-mail with Phone' supervision. A guide to homeopathic and supervisory assessment relevant to these contexts is included.

The polarity between 'vital' as 'energetic' and 'kit' as tools for the trade or survival rations, is in play in this section — The practice is grounded in some detail.

MAKING AND MAINTAINING WORKING RELATIONSHIP

Contracting

Before we practice or do supervision or indeed take part in any helping relationship we need to make the time and space for it. Sounds obvious except we are often so 'time poor' we get into trouble just through not making the time to be really present.

Contracting means clarifying intention, checking out expectations and getting alongside (see C.E.P. — Competence, Expectation and Process). It is a process in that while some elements are fixed others are moving moment to moment. Some items are written down, such as appointment times, fees and availability, making a 'hard' contract. Other elements, such as expectations and competence, change all the time. These are the 'soft' aspects of the contracting. Taking the time to get more aware of what is happening moment to moment keeps us alongside.

What use is it to stick to an initial contract, for a remedy for a blocked nose let's say, if as a client I have now identified a general blocking of the way ahead and want to address that instead? How to move the contract along? And what if we as practitioners perceive something more vital to address in the course of the relationship and yet this is not being requested by the client? Checking out what is happening to see that we are still alongside each other is a natural part of making and maintaining a functional working relationship. (See C.E.P. for guidance; also Page and Wosket, 1994; Hewson, 1999b)

Looking after relationship can be called making a 'working alliance.'

Working Alliance

A working alliance is the meta or supervisory perspective. It allows us to continue in a relationship even when difficulties arise or expectations change and we cannot get alongside each other — I am expecting to go one way and you another. We may feel personally challenged and yet we can continue on because we are making something we can trust to develop and change. Challenge and resistance are par for the course. Making and maintaining working relationship is a continual and dynamic process. In a therapeutic or supervisory hour, taking a few moments at the beginning and again at the end to check in and then review, signals the intention to cultivate a supervisory perspective — a place to go and comment on what is happening rather than just react to it. (See Checking in to a Group, Chapter Four, 'Ain't Gonna Die for You.)

Three Cornered Contracting

Three are always present;

Supervisor – Supervisee – Client.

Student – Supervisor – College.

Practitioner – Client – Client's world / Practitioner's world including remedy, etc.

Leaving anyone or anything out of the loop can tend either to isolation or to over dependence on one relationship. This systemic view (see 'Introduction,' An Inclusive Approach and Chapter Three, 'Cheetah'), invites us to take into account other relationships affecting the one we are currently in. We get a bigger picture. In supervision the client is always present. Supervising a student means assessment and an educational institution are in the loop. In practice, for example as a homeopath; patient, homeopath and remedy are present.

Drawing the scenario as a series of triads; painting in the lines more or less strongly, drawing triads as more or less regular, highlights, very fast, both how strong or weak and how near or distant the relationships are. (See Sculpting, Chapters Three and Four.)

Locating where working alliances are strong and where they need some attention can often be the clue to resolving an apparently 'stuck' case.

Five Point Contracting:
Guides to making and maintaining working relationship

1. Making a fitting space and time to focus on the work. This includes ground rules, frequency, duration, availability, 'out of hours' and partnership or locum arrangements, cancellations and fees. Writing the 'hard' contract.

2. Getting clear about our intentions and expectations in being in the relationship moment to moment. 'Soft' contracting (see C.E.P., next section.)

3. Being clear about commitment, boundaries and flexibility in a way homeopathic to each unique relationship. What is fixed and what mutable?

4. Being clear about accountability including when things go wrong. Who else needs to know what is happening here? Ongoing and end reporting and assessment. Where is the independent supervisory perspective on this relationship to come from?

5. Making time in session to reflect on the working relationship and re-contracting on considering what is working and what isn't. Making and maintaining a working alliance.

Attending to making and maintaining working relationship means whatever the task in hand, we are more likely to move with ease.

Mapping the Process 1

Maps and models help locate us in the process. Sharing these is ethical practice in that it promotes autonomy and relatedness. It doesn't help to work in confidence if one person is mapping the journey and the other is stumbling along behind them.

C.E.P. (next section) is a relational model with a focus on expectation, adaptability and change.

Mappa Mundi (See Chapter Six) brings awareness to the elemental movement; mapping it through metaphor.

Hawkins and Shohet's (2000) Seven Eyed or Double Matrix model attends to process.

Carroll has made the Seven Tasks of Supervision. (1996)

Elizabeth Holloway brings us the Systemic SAS model. (1995)

Page and Wosket's (1994) Cyclical model structures the time and space. (See 'Vital Kit, Contexts' Phone and E-mail Supervision — Mapping the Process 2)

These generic models, and others, map the terrain in different ways. All are congruent with a homeopathic approach to supervision and a supervisory approach to practice.

C.E.P. — Competence, Expectation and Process

This model attends to relationship. It is informed by a supervisory perspective and homeopathic principle.

It is a map designed to help locate dis-ease and stuckness which, while not yet articulated, can nonetheless prevent free movement. It is an aid to working alliance; a shared map we can each refer to in order to support or challenge a felt-sense that *"something isn't quite right."*

The mnemonic 'CREATES' is a reminder that there may be the possibility of recreating relationship by raising awareness of what it is we expect to happen and noticing how fixed or not we are in that expectation.

COMPETENCE is considered to be what we already do to adapt ourselves and our knowledge base to meet the challenge of each unique situation. To survive at all we are all competent, that is, adapt in our own way. The questions include:

Clarity: Of intention: What do I intend in being here? What do I do already that adapts to the needs of this situation? How do I intend to adapt the situation to my needs? What moves me in being here? Where is my compassion? What am I being asked for and what am I asking? How do I know these things? How do I check out my perceptions?

Realness: How real am I in this relationship? How at ease with myself? How present? Where is the edge of discomfort? What does that feel like? What do I censure in order to be here? What adaptation am I making? How free am I to occupy the full range of my competence? How do my expressions and interventions convey my real meanings and motivations? How in/congruent are they? And asking these questions in relation to the other? How real are they to me?

Empathy: What can I empathise with here? Where does my fellow feeling meet a wall? What prevents me getting alongside the situation / the other? Ignorance? Opposing belief? Different values? Lack of common experience? Simple aversion? etc. Where am I stuck in empathy? How free am I to move between myself and the other?

Acceptance: What is happening here? What does it look like? Feel like? What is my sense of it? What do I think of it? What is my response? Where am I in this relationship on a continuum between unconditionally accepting and totally rejecting what or who is here?

Technical competence: What are the theories, maps, models and practices in play here? What is my competence in using them? How do I adapt them to meet the needs of this unique relationship? What is the minimum intervention here that gets alongside? How is my technical knowledge shared between us? How transparent is my use of it? How does my experience here add to the body of knowledge of the community to which I belong?

Ethical practice: What are the ethical and professional issues here? What values and beliefs am I bringing? How do I relate to the values and beliefs of the other(s)?

Stillness: What is the energetic quality in this relationship? How am I 'being' as opposed to what I am 'doing'? Where is the still point between us? What is that like?

EXPECTATIONS we each bring to relationship are more or less explicit, owned and shared. They are realised, developed and changed in the process. Questions arising include:

Clarity: How clear or not are the expectations brought to this relationship? About the roles? The tasks? What have we explicitly contracted for and what is assumed? How do I recognise the expectations that have not been articulated? What expectations do I have that I have not shared? How are these expectations changing moment to moment?

Realness: How realistic are the expectations I am aware of? What can I realistically expect?

Empathy: Do I expect empathy? Do I expect to feel empathy? What is this expectation preventing me from actually feeling?

Acceptance: How open, willing, able am I to expect the unexpected in this relationship?

Technical Competence: What can I expect of myself in relation to the role and tasks? What level of supervision, peer support, teaching, coaching or mentoring do I need in order to adapt, develop or change what I know to meet the unique demands of this relationship?

Ethical Practice: What are the ethical issues I might expect to arise in this relationship? What are these expectations based on? What is expected of me in response?

Stillness: In considering the quality of this relationship, where might I expect to find the still point? What needs to happen, what minimum intervention needs be made, to return to the still point?

PROCESS Is made up of tasks. (Carroll 1996) Competence and Expectations are realised, developed and changed in the process of the relationship. The questions include:

Clarity: What are the roles and tasks in this relationship? How clear am I about my roles and tasks? How do these relate to others I am involved in? What do we need to know about each other? Who am I accountable to and for what?

Realness: Where have we lost touch with the roles and tasks? Where are we on task? What else is present? What is more real to each of us than the roles and tasks we are each here to respond to?

Empathy: How much do I empathise or not with the roles and tasks? What is the quality of the space between us? How am I getting alongside or not? How near or apart are we? What is the feeling? What does the space look like? What is it characterised by?

Acceptance: How am I keeping to my role and task? What am I trying to do? What am I trying to change? What am I forcing? What don't I accept?

Technical Competence: What is happening to my theories, maps and models in responding to the tasks? What is developing, changing or being realised?

Ethical Practice: How do I assess the tasks and roles ethically? What is happening to my beliefs and values? How at ease with the process am I? Where is the edge of discomfort? What is that like? What is it telling me?

Stillness: What is my experience of stillness in the fulfilment of these tasks? What is the quality of activity? How are we moving?

What is the story we are co-creating here ?

GUIDES FOR TRIADING:
Working in Threes

Setting the Scene

Three are always present: Patient, Practitioner and Remedy (proving made by many people); Client, Therapist and their particular therapeutic modality; Practitioner, Supervisor and Client.

Practicing in a triad in order to inquire into the dynamics of practice, is a vital part of the Kit.

Whether as two and an empty chair, a peer supervision group, a student class or whole conference you can inquire into the dynamics of practice by working in threes.

Typically, chairs are set to represent each role. Participants move in and out of these in order to experience the different perspectives. Assigning role to a chair rather than person helps with getting in and out of role too.

In order to participate fully we needs be vulnerable to the experience. This may leave us with nerves exposed, upset feelings and a recreation of shame.

The following guides are designed to help facilitators and participants alike to make the most of the practice in creating a safe enough, risky enough, space.

• It is a good idea to clarify the purpose of the triad exercise each time.

• Guidance over the nature and scope of a presenting issue could be discussed in the group first.

• Confidentiality could be discussed with each new group. What does it take for people to join in with confidence?

• Setting up each triad is the first task. This involves contracting for roles, confidentiality, feedback, time boundary and time out. (See 'Vital Kit, Making Working Relationship.')

• Offering permission to not participate at this time or to limit participation to particular roles can be helpful. If joining in generally is an issue for a participant, then working initially in a pair can help introduce the possibilities of more dynamic work. Observing the rest of the group practicing in threes is a good place to start.

• A 'Working Journal' ('Vital Kit, Contexts') could be suggested as a way to unload and reflect on issues that arise during triad work.

• Participants could be offered extra time at the end of the exercise to work in another triad or pair to facilitate moving on.

• Disbanding a triad is its last task. This may not happen until feedback to the larger group is given, signalling the completion of that round of practice.

• Checking in and out of roles by saying your name and 'returning' to the room is often all that is needed to complete any unfinished business.

We are each responsible for what we bring to the work. Clarify at the beginning what help is on hand to resolve, contain and refer issues arising.

Functions of Triad Practice

• To sit in role as Presenter (client or supervisee for example), Receiver (practitioner or supervisor for example) and Observer (observing aspect of self)

• To practice moving in and out of role, encouraging empathy with each position.

• To develop awareness of the nature of formal space and time — clarifying intention, making and maintaining working relationship, contracting, working with time limitation, boundaries, flexibility, focus and effective use of the space.

• To practice being present.

• To practice the art of active listening, getting alongside and minimal intervention.

• To develop an awareness of the energetic nature of relationship.

• To develop self awareness of affective presence in relationship.

• To develop self awareness of the nature and consequences of particular interventions eg open and closed questions, reflections, advice, mirroring, modelling, etc.

• To practice the art of compassionate inquiry.

• To practice observation with acceptance — to describe what is happening rather than what we think should be happening.

• To encourage giving and receiving respectful feedback.

Facilitating Practice in Threes

How useful working in threes is as an inquiry into practice depends largely upon the willingness of the group to participate in formal practice, the clarity of the focus and relevance of the task to the group.

The competence, that is adaptability, (C.E.P. in 'Vital Kit, Making Working Relationship') of the facilitator in 'getting alongside' and holding the process — including emotional fall-out, confusion about role or task and resistance to joining in, can be the difference between banal and trivial work and meaningful inquiry.

How to 'get alongside' a whole group and each individual in it, how to acknowledge the 'urge to merge' and 'the need to separate,' while making elegant and minimal energetic interventions to assist the process, is the decidedly ambitious and idealised task of the group facilitator of dynamic group practice. In reality we bumble along, making a more or less 'good enough' job of it; noticing this here and drawing attention to it, missing that there, fusing with the state here and holding an overview for a moment there. (See Group Facilitator as Story Teller in Chapter Four.)

Working in twos and threes as facilitators, especially in large groups, greatly enlarges the possibilities for meta-comment and story making as well as enhancing the enjoyment and usefulness of the experience for group and facilitator. Making a working relationship with facilitation is a primary task. (See to 'Vital Kit, Making Working Relationship.')

Facilitator or Group Supervisor is a role that may be allocated to one person. This is usual in a student group, or at times in practice when we want the 'outsider' perspective of the skilled group supervisor. In peer groups, the role may be rotated among group participants. Alternatively, the whole group may take on the role, exploring each one's contribution to facilitation as a part of the inquiry.

Roles and Tasks

The basic roles in a triad are Presenter, Receiver and Observer. These are aspects of self in role. The Presenter may be a supervisee or client. The Receiver may be a practitioner, therapist or supervisor. The Observer is our observing aspect. A triad can be set to explore any relationship.

Presenter

Presenter brings a story. This may be in the shape of a 'case.' It may be their own story in relation to a client or practice or to their studies. It may be a moment in practice giving pause for thought. It may be a 'felt-sense' of something that can't yet be got a hold of.

The task is to bring something with enough 'bite' in it to be alive in the room and yet not so big and unknown to the Presenter that it may overwhelm the resources of a time limited learning exercise. Triading has a learning focus. Healing happens. Catharsis happens. Feelings are aired and shared. E-motional shifts are made. The intention is to raise awareness.

This is not always such an easy line to draw, between a therapeutic and a learning encounter and the most seemingly innocuous material can pack a powerful punch when told to an active listener, especially with the benefit of additional alert observation. It is for these reasons that guidance to facilitation and working relationship is important.

Receiver

The Receiver practices actively listening to the presenter. (See Active Listening in Chapter Two, 'Let's Go Fly a Kite.') The task is to help the presenter clarify, resolve or re-frame the story they are bringing. The questions in the context of a homeopathic approach are:

a) What happens to move the story along in being present and alive to the moment?

b) When anything at all needs to be done, how effective in moving the story along, is a minimal and energetic intervention that gets alongside the story teller?

Being observed in practice can be an excruciating experience, taking us back to the self-consciousness of the child. Making a good enough working relationship with ourselves, presenter and observer is needed in order to get anything from this practice besides a feeling perhaps of paralysis and incompetence. The quality of observation practiced goes a long way to resolving any difficulty here.

Observer

The Observer role is an opportunity to practice the observing aspect of the practitioner. While engaged in being either the Giver or Receiver it can be all too easy to merge with the story, to lose sight of what is happening in the interaction. The Observer is akin to the supervisory quality of looking — to observe without attachment to outcomes, accepting what is actually present.

This is a compassionate inquiry. The Observer is holding, with respect, the space between Presenter and Receiver. The first task is to pay attention to any inclination towards persecution of the presenting and receiving pair. Owning this vulnerability in feedback, the observer can help to dispel any fears the receiver has of being judged. The observer's own vulnerability can throw light too on the case in hand since everything that happens in the formal space of the triad may well prove relevant to the issue or case presented. The case doesn't stay neatly in the box between Presenter and Receiver after all — like a cold, any of the rest of us may be susceptible to it.

The Observer pays attention to what is happening in the 'here and now.' The task is to be as present as possible and to describe simply what is perceived (see below Observers in a whole group triad). It is not the Observer's task to judge the performance. The Presenter benefits from the Observer's feedback to Receiver in being there to listen to it.

The task is to observe and feed back, to the Receiver, what is happening in the interaction, and specifically what the responses to the Receiver's interventions are. In this way, observation is offered in the interests of the Receiver's increasing self awareness in role (see 'Feedback' below).

The Observer doesn't intervene in the action between the Presenter and Receiver during the session. In waiting until the end, the Observer is again encouraged to stay in role and not be tempted to become another Receiver.

Whole Group Triading

A whole group may participate in one grand triad.

Additional Roles

Other roles are satellites around this core; making a network of triads, each with it's own energy field and each contributing to the bigger picture.

For example, there may also be 'Shadow,' 'Empty Chair' (see Chapter Two 'Let's Go Fly a Kite'), 'Greek Chorus' (See Chapter Four, 'Ain't Gonna Die for You'), and additional Observers.

Any of these extra roles can be invited to join in the play by the core triad or at the suggestion of the facilitator. They are all feedback roles and as such are guided by intention to assist the Receiver and Presenter in their task. (See Feedback Guides below.)

Empty Chair

The 'Empty Chair' represents any parties to the relationship not actually present — for example client or remedy picture or significant other in the client's story or any other part of the client-practitioner-supervisor story. Either the Presenter or Receiver may volunteer or invite each other to occupy the empty chair. The task is to give voice to another element of the story.

Shadow

The participant in role as Shadow is tasked to try voicing or acting the unspoken or unexpressed elements of the story belonging to the person or interaction they are shadowing. (See Chapter Four, 'Ain't Gonna Die for You.') Shadow is listening to what is not being said but which is nonetheless being expressed. Shadow can exaggerate hand and other movements as well as put words to what is felt in an attempt to convey some less consciously articulated aspects of the story. (For example in Chapter Four, Shadow's outstretched arms expressing in a gesture the essence of the Presenter's story.)

Shadow comes into play once a group is used to working together and can take more of a risk in getting it wrong, making a fool and generally having fun. The Shadow walks a fine line between taking over the roles shadowed to *"do it the way I would do it"* and offering some insight in the service of the participants. For example, if I am shadowing a Receiver who is passively listening, who perhaps looks a bit 'all at sea' at the complexity of what she is receiving in a torrent from the Presenter, I might offer, *"I am drowning. Help me! I'm losing control of the boat here, I'm going under, etc."*

The Receiver can pay attention to their shadow, ignore it, take up a metaphor and run with it or revise it to express more closely their actual experience.

The Presenter in hearing the Receiver's shadow, for example, can also hear its relevance or not to the story they are telling. Stories *are* co-created. This exercise simply makes the process more explicit.

Most often it is the Shadow and Observers who perceive the more elemental story and who express the e-motions involved. This is possibly because the Presenter and Receiver are engaged in a relationship and attached to the narrative as told. The Shadow and other Observers are free from that responsibility and can attend to the playful and the observing aspects of themselves, freely expressing what is there rather than worrying about what to do next.

In this way, though it may seem a complex waste of time to set up a triad, in fact, once proficient in the practice, it is more often a most effective and efficient way to cut to the chase.

Greek Chorus

'Greek Chorus' is a number of participants tasked to support one of the roles or the whole triad, in making the voice already present bigger or clearer or with more feeling or with movement — see to Chapter Four, 'Ain't Gonna Die for You' when the whole group spontaneously becomes a 'Greek Chorus' in making a song, drumming and dance to support the emerging story.

Observers

In addition to 'Shadows' and 'Greek Chorus,' Observers in a whole group triad arrange themselves nearer or farther away from the Presenter, Receiver and main Observer. They can then focus on one of the many interactions in play in the story telling and listening: Observing and listening empathetically, chair pulled up, open to the feelings e-motions being expressed, or, observing and listening in a more detached way, chair far back and with a wider view of the whole interaction.

Individual Observers might focus on:

• The story itself; it's spontaneity, clarity, characteristics, anything strange, rare and peculiar, themes and connections, polarities and resonances with bigger stories.

• The language the story is told in.

• Where the silences come and where the stillness is and what quality it brings. Where silences are the same as stillness and where they are not.

• The interventions the Listener makes and what happens in response.

• The body movements of Presenter and Listener, including how they mirror each other. Specific focus on hand gestures.

• The pace of the session.

• The affective quality of the relationship between Presenter and Receiver — what is it characterised by?

• What the felt-sense of the session is and where that is located physically with the Observer e.g. tension in the muscles, breath holding, etc.

These are some of the many aspects Observers can focus on. In a student practice or live clinical setting (see 'Vital Kit, Contexts') participants can choose or be guided to focus on an aspect they need some practice in.

Dual Roles

Negotiating dual roles is an ordinary everyday experience; relationships naturally involve a complex weaving of different roles. In therapeutic or supervisory relationship however, awareness of dual roles and their impact on the work is elemental to the task.

In practicing under supervision it's probably a good idea to avoid dual roles. Simply put, if something goes wrong in the relationship to the extent that you want to leave, then if that person is your supervisor you have only one new relationship to find. If they are also your teacher or tutor then you have two to find. It can never be a good idea (never say never) to make of your practitioner your supervisor since you may find your vulnerability as a client unwittingly used against you in a learning or assessment situation. On the other hand, it is quite possible to negotiate dual roles to good purpose, since while being as much ourselves as we can be, we are not the role since role creates an *aesthetic distance:*

"I don't feel cared for by you as you are not so available by phone as I need you to be."

It is me as a practitioner who is being addressed here — I am not being told that I am an uncaring person full stop.

In triading, in attending to one role at a time, we are exploring the nature of each one in practice. We are clarifying intention, sharpening focus and exploring how flexible and responsive we are in each role.

We get in role and on task. We find out how we do that in giving and receiving feedback.

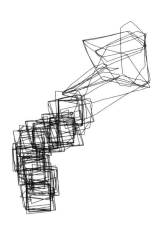

The Art of Useful Feedback

What does it matter if we are right in what we say if we can't be heard? To be useful feedback needs to be both heard and acted upon.

Homeopathic feedback gets alongside, is minimal and energetic – It hits the spot in other words, and without so much as force to cause a defensive reaction.

The simplest way to achieve this is to get clear about intention.

Who is this feedback for? What is it's purpose?

To make me look clever/ insightful/wise/creative?

To make me liked by them?

To make the other do it differently?

To do their job for them?

To make the other feel better?

To be careful not to offend?

Or are we intending to 'wake us up' to what is happening? To see as far and wide and deep as we can, to enable choices to be made, for the other to do it in their own way, to move in their own unique fashion, at their own pace and in their own direction.

To give useful feedback is humbling — we put ourselves aside in the interests of another's journey. To receive it is humbling too in that we put aside our grandiose idea of who we are and see ourselves instead as others do. It is liberating too — no longer the story of phony omnipotence but the flawed and most interesting tale of the fellow traveller.

Feedback is given tentatively by inquiring into what is happening since we know it is only the way we see it and maybe not the way it is for the other. Feedback is no less challenging for being tentative, since to see things at all from the point of view of another can be as profoundly unsettling as it is potentially liberating.

To receive useful feedback is a gift we sometimes find hard to accept.

Feedback is asking questions:

"What is it you are doing?" " Where are you going with this?" " What are the obstacles in your way?"

"From my observing position, can I see anything else of the path ahead?"

"How can I help draw any of this to your attention?"

"What has been drawn to my attention in observing this interaction?"

"Where is the movement?"

"What is being expressed and how?"

"Can I model it differently? Can I mirror what I see and thereby show it to you?"

"Can I catch what you are doing and throw it back to you in metaphor, movement or song for example?"

As Shadow *"Can I articulate something not 'there' yet?"*

As Greek chorus *"Can I support your voice?"*

As facilitator *"Can I suggest a way of playing with this or set a scene or structure?"*

"How can I reflect this back to you?"

An effective mnemonic for remembering the characteristics of useful feedback is CORBS (Hawkins and Shohet, 2000)

Clear — We are open to misunderstandings – check it out.

Owned — My perspective rather than a universal truth.

Regular — Rather than stored up as a big event.

Balanced — Awareness of tendency to please or criticise.

Specific — It is this we are talking about not everything.

Receiving Feedback

It won't kill you. If it comes in the wrong package — too harsh, too bland, mis-understands you, is plain wrong-headed — it is still an opportunity to learn something — else drop it on the floor and leave it there — it isn't yours after all…

It's a good idea to repeat what you have heard — it is amazing how often we don't even remember what has been said just a moment ago but hear instead what we expected to.

"When I said that the Presenter changed tack after your intervention what have I just told you?"

"That I talk too much?"

In the triad, the Presenter has the last word when the Observers have given their feedback to the Receiver and they in turn have checked it out. In this way, the Presenter can bring these additional insights to their story.

Finally, the Facilitator(s) in conversation with the triad or group, hold the 'as if one story' in making the connections, noticing disconnections, themes, questions and patterns in story and movement that have been observed by everyone. The task of Group facilitator, or Supervisor (terms used interchangeably in this context) is akin to that of Proving Co-ordinator who is holding the 'as if one' story of the remedy emerging from the different provers' experiences of the potentised substance.

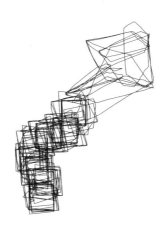

Voices

"Do I contradict myself?
Very well, I contradict myself.
(I am large. I contain multitudes.)"
Walt Whitman

The ancient gods illustrate something of our complex and contradictory natures. They are invoked here as a means for us to explore the e-motions we bring to practice and the core activity of giving and receiving feedback.

Aphrodite goddess of love — Who is seducing whom? Where is the love?

Artemis goddess of the moon and of the hunt — How do I reflect? What 'right answers' do I hunt for?

Asclepius god of medicine and killed by Zeus for disturbing the world order! What ill can come from my good intentions?

Athena goddess of war and of wise counsel — What or who am I fighting for? How am I doing this? What advice do I give myself?

Atlas — shouldering the world. How do I carry my responsibility? How lightly? How much of a weight is it?

Cheiron the centaur educator, half human and half horse, the wounded healer — How do I acknowledge the wound? How do I acknowledge my animal nature?

Demeter goddess of the birth of the world — What are we giving birth to here? What is arising? How am I nurturing my own needs? How am I looking after the other?

Dyonisus god of the vines — What aspects of my own nature do I censure in my professional role? The fun? The relaxing? The celebration? How do I respond to images, impulses and intuitions spontaneously arising?

Hades god of the underworld — How do I respond to the 'shadow' material? How / Do I stay with the shadow? Bring light to the shadows?

Helios god of Light — In what light am I observing?

Hephaestus god of fire and art — What inspires me? What am I creating here? What are we co-creating?

Hera goddess of marriage, punishing infidelity while herself Zeus's secret lover — Where and how am I being in /congruent? What is revealed and what hidden? What is hypocritical in my relationship to you?

Hermes messenger of the gods and bearer of dead souls — symbol of transformation through death to life. How do I bring/ receive the 'bad' as well as the 'good' news? How do I accept the news brought to me? What do I need to die to? What change am I being asked to make?

Hestia goddess of family peace and a virgin — What is in conflict here? What is the peaceful intervention? What is untried here between us?

Iacchus god directing the ceremony of initiation — What is being initiated here? What is my role in this rite of passage?

Perseus the hero who accidentally killed his father — Who or what is in charge here? Where is the containment? What do we need to die to in order to restore free movement?

Priapus god of fertility — What is potent in this encounter? Where is the power between us? How am I enabling another to grow? Where is the sterility?

Poseidon god of the sea — How ready to 'go with the flow' am I? What is the feeling here?

Zeus god of gods, maintaining justice over all — How do I respond to all these voices? Is one as valuable as another? How is my practice good enough?

In acknowledging the many voices we bring to our practice, the ones we tend to allow and those we censor, we go some way to accepting their impact on ourselves and others.

CONTEXTS

Now to put these guidelines into practice in different contexts…

Self Supervising

Supervision, as a quality of looking, is that aspect of ourselves that sits with 'what is'. In professional helping and healing, we give someone else the task of supervising us, sometimes called mentoring in non therapeutic settings (see Introduction, Supervision, Mentoring and Coaching). At the same time, we are developing our own internal supervising voices; our 'supervisory selves' (see Voices in 'Vital Kit, Guides for Triading.').

We know that complete reliance on ourselves can lead to isolation, narcissism, 'me and them ism'. Independence is one thing, the ability to make decisions in complex, difficult and dark circumstances. This is our art. Independence with relatedness looks quite different from acting in isolation.

When it comes to taking care of ourselves, we can tend to either over dose or neglect ourselves. In only self supervising, this could mean we end up with the critical

"Never good enough"

or the blithe voice of

"I'm OK, oops I've tripped over…"

Dynamic Self Supervising and Reflection

Developing a reflective habit is a survival tool for anyone let alone for someone setting up shop as a helper. If we intend to survive, thrive and flourish we had better develop the capacity to reflect. Any relationship can be a healing one if we are able to reflect on who we are and what we are doing in it, how we are seen by each other and what it is we are creating together — peace would break out wouldn't it? Since it doesn't, it must be harder to do than that— the motive force hidden, wittingly or not. Reflection is not enough. Not everything yields itself up to the light.

Dynamic Self-supervising includes reflection and goes further to re-create scenarios in art-play in order to reveal, at an aesthetic distance, something of the elemental nature of the interaction. That something which cannot be communicated in rational thought and word alone but is rather captured in essence in something else — another form; a metaphor, play, poem, drawing, remedy, movement or ritual. (See Reflective to Dynamic Practice in Chapter Three, 'Cheetah.')

The activities throughout this book are designed to reach this more elemental level of inquiry in appealing to our sense of play. Through art-play we find our own voices in which to write our own stories.

Who is Supervising Me Today?

Supervision is a quality of looking; without attachment, at what is happening. This is an aspirational practice. It's a curious thing that we are more likely to come closer to it when supervising or practicing for another than when we are self supervising (or self healing.) Our voices may be anything but compassionate and inquiring.

This is probably why practicing a healing art or supervision is self-healing. It is an opportunity to be loving, to be compassionate, to accept unconditionally what we find.

"I am never more well than when I am practicing."

"Practice keeps me sane."

we say.

(Note, not over working, taking inappropriate responsibility, allowing practice to impoverish us in any way, working completely in isolation — it isn't any old practice that heals!)

Just about the only work I can stand to do when I give myself a migraine (now why would anyone do that?) is to see patients. It takes me out of myself. Sometimes my self-supervising voice is my headache.

John Towler (2001) asks

"Which Sub-Personality is Supervising Today?"

Making working relationship with our inner voices is the primary task of self supervision.

Who talks to you? (See Voices in 'Vital Kit, Triading') How do you learn? (See Experience of Learning in Chapter Five, 'Magic Glasses.')

Who is supervising me today?

Who tells me my stories?

What voices do they use?

Physical? feeling? Sensing? thinking?

Who are they talking to?

What are they telling me?

What do they need in response?

How do I listen to them?

What do I do with the stories?

What are my impressions of my story telling and listening selves?

If I imagine they are my children, these story tellers and listeners within me, how do I look after them and guide them? What are they teaching me?

What kind of working relationship do I have with them?

Where is the compassion between us?

Self supervision is an ongoing conversation, a regular practice to suit individual temperament and timetable in order to let what is happening first sink in, and later, in its own time, re-emerge as knowledge, understanding, and in practice, clinical wisdom. Its strength is that we can always be there for ourselves, we often aren't but we could be. The flip side might be isolation, narcissism and wilfulness.

The exercises throughout the book are intended to help develop our observing selves —- and in so doing let loose our shadows, mischief-makers and judges in all their guises. Self supervising is getting to know ourselves in different contexts — and we could add, learning how to love who we find there.

Group Supervision

In group Supervision, at the other end of the continuum from self supervising, we are invited to see ourselves as others do and experience practice from another's perspective: We receive feedback we don't necessarily recognise and take an active interest in practicing in ways we don't choose to work.

The exercises in the book are generally relevant to good working relationships in groups. See Chapters Three and Four for demonstrations and guidance in dynamic group supervisions. Seeactivities: 'Sculpture' (Chapters Three and Four) 'Checking in' and Group Orchestra and Choir (both Chapter Four). See 'Vital Kit, Guides for Triading.'

Organisations, Teams and Networks

People become a group when there is membership, boundary and interdependence. (Thompson 1999) We also work in groups that are teams, networks and organisations. Each has their specific issues with working relationship and all involve three cornered contracting. (See 'Vital Kit, Making and Maintaining Working Relationship.')

Networks hold more loosely together than other groups or teams. Some aren't groups at all by the definition referred to here. They have their own peculiar issues in that they don't necessarily meet face to face, frequently have fluid boundaries and don't support each other very much. However, they still share identity and purpose, role and task very often. Members of a professional organisation for example may meet in different combinations at conference or seminar but not work together over time. Networks of supervisors around a college may meet once for induction and training or annually for a 'refresher,' working individually with students the rest of the time. Supervising networks means working with individuals and groups in the newtork to clarify the common purpose, ethic, roles and tasks and making those explicit and available to everyone. Making opportunity to meet, phone and e-mail each other as well as making written guidance for the work can help networkers feel a part of a team even while working largely independently.

A group is greater than the sum of its parts. It has a life of its own. Holding the individual needs in relation to the needs of the group is the primary task of group supervision and facilitation, in other words, staying with the 'urge to merge' and 'the need to separate.' (See Chapter Four.) A team explicitly puts the group needs over that of any one individual; being a 'team player' being the most prized characteristic.

Every group develops its own culture, those things we share and take for granted and that let us know we are 'us' and they are 'not us.' The ties that bind also keep us apart from others — and as we have said all along separation is the root of dis-ease. The value of a group facilitator or an organisational supervisor from outside the group, as an independent and time limited visitor, is in being able to look without attachment at how we relate; how the culture is developing and being maintained, who or what it is serving, who it excludes and where it might lead.

Systems

A systems perspective takes account of the contexts in which we live, work and make our stories; the complex matrix of relationships we bring to this encounter. A systemic approach is essential for considering the life of a group, network, team or organisation. If anyone is left out of the picture, for example if students are encouraged to reflect and practice under supervision while the college faculty acts without taking time to consider its role, then a polarised 'us' and 'them' tends to fix itself in place of a dynamic relationship between staff and students. In supervising any organisation, a conversation with everyone, and especially managers, needs to develop.

A systemic approach is congruent with ethical practice in that it encourages inclusion — each matrix connecting to another to make bigger and bigger pictures. It tends towards dissolving 'us' and 'them,' holding instead the relationship between individual and wider collective. In homeopathy, studying remedies in groups; miasmatic, plant families or on the periodic table, demonstrates the effectiveness of a systemic approach in clearly defining both individual characteristics and common elements.

Conflict

Conflict is attended to within a systems perspective by translating tendencies to blame, pathologise and scapegoat into an inquiry into the needs being expressed. The intention is to look for ways in which the needs of different people in the system as well as the system needs can be brought into relationship with each other. The 'transforming triad' (see Chapter Four) comes in here as a model to assist with turning around a culture of shame and blame to become one in which we own our vulnerabilities, take our power and reflect on the consequences. (Carroll, 2000 and Hawkins, 2002)

Live Clinical
Group Supervision:
A Model for Bare Foot practice 1

Live Clinical Supervision

This is akin to triad practice except that here we are 'performing' with a real client or patient and that is a stage set to bring all the shadows, judges and mischief-makers out of the closet. (Triad practice is 'forming,' 'storming' and 'norming' while practice is 'performing' — or more truly continual rehearsal.)

We do live clinical supervision to model practice, to give beginning practitioners and supervisors a chance to develop their own style with the benefit of feedback and to give clients greater care and attention than might be possible at times when alone with a novice practitioner or indeed with a routinised experienced one.

In live clinical supervision we are all on our mettle!

'Vital Kit, Guides to Making Working Relationship' and 'Triading' are designed to be helpful in setting up a live clinical practice under supervision.

I want to focus here on how the triad works in clinical situations in which a whole group is present either to learn from observing a practitioner at work or to take turns in practice. The scenario is then complicated by making this a 'barefoot' situation, one in which there are limited or unusual resources; for example students have gathered together to learn with a clinical supervisor who may not share their language or local knowledge — as in the Botswana Homeopathic Project to whom this book is dedicated. Maybe a 'Children's Clinic' is being run by volunteers at a school or community centre, or a College Student Clinic is attending to several functions at the same time. In each of these cases, apparent distraction from practice can be turned around to support the task of presenting, receiving and observing the elemental story.

The strength of limitation: 'Bare foot' practice — The language barrier in a multilingual setting encourages listening at a more elemental level. The act of translation also encourages this in slowing the action down. The unfamiliar places we meet in clinic at times, can mean we are taken out of our comfort zones and put on a learning edge. I remember one student clinic in Belgrade being held in a sports centre bar where cigarette smoke filled the air, people wandered across the scene lugging holdalls and the walls were plastered with near naked bodies beautiful. We had to work harder to create a focussed space for the clinic until we were aware only of each case magically forming between client, student practitioner and the alert observation of the group. The smoke, badminton players and glossy bodies all floated out of sight.

The apparent chaos of student training in a children's clinic with each child attended by adults and siblings and staffed by volunteers with a wide variation in skill, experience and need, can help us to 'work outside the box' of the quiet one-to-one consultation. Each person with their task becomes a part of the unfolding drama of the case — if the supervision is sufficiently observing and accepting of the whole scenario. The elemental story or 'case' can emerge in surprising places — with the 'clinic Administrator' who is making the appointment, with the people playing with the children while they wait their turn for consultation and with the Observers paying attention to what is being spontaneously said and done.

A College Clinic is a great place to begin each session afresh; to interrupt the story with each new student group and supervisor, all bringing their own styles and insights. A College Clinic can teach multi-tasking and working with dual roles as it attends to learning, practicing, teaching, supervising and assessing.

How are these different clinics set up so that the formal practice triad is maintained while the characteristic functions and tasks of each clinic are accomplished?

In any supervision the homeopathic aim must be to make the minimum, similar and energetic intervention to restore autonomy and relatedness— and get out of there before a dependence on 'experts' is created. A 'barefoot' situation, where we are out of the comfort zone of a one-to-one consultation in a space designed for the purpose, challenges our competence (adaptability) in staying in role and on task.

Roles in Live Clinical Group Supervision

The basic roles in a live group supervised clinic are as for Triading plus some extras. All can be adapted for any situation and number in either assigning individuals to multi-tasking and dual roles or more than one person to the same task or role — In 'bare-foot' situations shortage of people is not usually the issue so that the task is more likely finding useful jobs for everyone.

Here we look at a training situation in which there are many students and only one clinic supervisor who is also teacher and group facilitator. In situations in which we are practicing with little time and many patients then recruiting untrained volunteers into defined roles and tasks will also ease the work and reap rewards greater than the sum of the parts.

Presenter: Now a real client.

Receiver: Either a practitioner modelling practice for the group or else a student practicing being with a client or a novice supervisor practicing with a supervisee.

Observers: Each one focussing on aspects of the therapeutic/supervisory art of especial interest or difficulty. (See Whole Group Triading in 'Vital Kit, Triading' for development of this role.)

Group Supervisor: Setting the scene and roles, holding and articulating the process.

Plus

Translator: May be needed to Communicate between the client and group on the one hand and the supervisor on the other.

Recorders: One may be needed to take accurate notes of the consultation should the Receiver be a novice practitioner and the Supervisor not share the language. A video recording with a wide angle lens means the consultation will be available as a teaching aid too. In the absence of many trained practitioners, teachers and supervisors, visual and audio recordings become invaluable aids to learning — building up and sharing our libraries of recorded practice must be a primary task for practitioner, professional and educational organisations if good practice is to be modelled and made available everywhere it is needed. (See below 'Recording the Action.')

Minders and Carers: In children and family clinics taking care of the people who come with the client, or playing with the child who is client when the parents are telling their story, can support both Clients and Receiver who may be overwhelmed by the experience.

Clinic Administrator: Organises the smooth running of the clinic: Client appointments, introductions and contracting, room readiness, booking student groups and supervisors, arranging technical support and additional support people. Locating appropriate clients including making relationships with practitioners and agencies who may refer clients is a Clinic Administrator's primary task.

The live group clinical supervision starts to feel like assembling a film crew!

It might look like this in a homeopathic student context :

Client/Patient: Contracting — They need to be confident in the process; to know beforehand what everyone is here to do, how the consultation is to be recorded and how that record will be used. Whose client are they? Who is in charge of this consultation? Who do they speak to and who will not be engaging with them? How will the session be followed up? What is expected of them in a student clinic, for example are they being asked to return for a number of sessions?

Receivers and Observer tasks are as outlined in 'Vital Kit, Guides for Triading.'

Group Supervisor sets the scene, roles and tasks to suit the group and it's purposes. For example in a student training clinic in which no one common language is shared it might look like this:

A student practitioner is receiving the case of a same language presenting Client.

A **Recorder** is making a record of the consultation in the original language.

A **Translator** is making simultaneous verbal translation of the consultation for the benefit of the visiting Supervisor.

The mixed language student group are sharing the role of **Observer:** Those speaking the language are assigned the task of attending to original language, themes and expressions.

Some focus on images arising, colours, shapes. Others focus on the tone and quality of voice, the body language, the relationship between the Client and Practitioner as expressed in position and movement and their own 'felt sense' in observing the action.

The group is encouraged to explore senses, intuitions, instincts and feelings in response to actual observations.

Feedback

After the consultation the Supervisor asks the group to share their observations with the whole group, making distinction between simple observation and interpretation — for example:

"When the client put her hands together like this it was as if she might be pleading"

Simple observation: *"The client put her hands together like this."*

Interpretation: *"as if she might be pleading."*

The invitation is to check it out. The group might try exaggerating gestures which haven't been picked up during the consultation in order to suggest possible directions the story might be heading in.

The simple observations and questions for differentiation — alternative stories — are recorded by the Supervisor and translated for all to see. This might look like a list of words and phrases, shapes, pictures, colours, maps and models drawn and tacked up on a board like a collage. They are the 'sensation as if' of a whole group exposed to the story being created in the relationship between Client and Practitioner. Polarities, themes, characteristics may emerge.

The tendency for the more elemental story to be picked up complete by the observing group is striking. Not hearing or understanding the verbal story proves to be no barrier to getting its meaning. The e-motion expresses itself in movement, felt-sense and quality of relationship. The written record comes in to keep the observations grounded; to check them out against what was actually said and to assist in differential diagnoses.

On the occasions I have worked in this way, groups of student homeopaths as large as thirty and forty, speaking different languages and dialects, have become absorbed in the process. Each person has their own task and focus. Each is an important part of the whole and each one is learning something afresh and from their own experience and not just from observing an 'expert' do it.

Completing the Task

The task of listening to and making sense of the Client's story is accomplished. The Client can be enormously supported by the attentive focus of so many people. The homeopathic response becomes clearer. The possible differential stories are pointed up. Each participant has practiced an element of their healing art and experienced a real shift in energy and perception.

When we are working dynamically in this way we are developing the focus required of the practitioner and supervisor: To be present to the more energetic story while at the same time being fully engaged in relationship.

In bare-foot practice situations where there are few practitioners and many people needing help, then being awake to the moment and acting fast on what you perceive is essential. This dynamic student practitioner group training is a good preparation for this.

Sharing the Experience — Recording the Action

Videoing practice and with a wide angle lens, so that both the client and practitioner are visible, is a valuable tool for teaching as well as for self and peer supervision.

By including the practitioner in the action, the dynamics of the story making are revealed. We can see how naturally we mirror each other as we attempt to understand and to make ourselves understood. We can see more clearly what happens when we are alongside another and what it is like when we lose that rapport; how our interventions are resisted or ignored. 'Interrupting' a 'comfort story' shows in increased animation and expression.

This all becomes much clearer when we point the camera at ourselves in action as well as at the client — we see how we affect each other; how the tale is told between us.

Contracting properly for recording and use of records in future teaching and supervision is integral to the task.

After the lavish setting of the group supervised clinic, which is sophisticated in role and task, inclusive in making a place for everyone, no matter the level of skill or experience, phone and email supervision may seem rather under resourced; not so much a film crew in action as imagining the scene from reading the script alone!

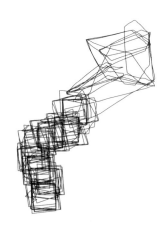

Phone and E-mail Supervision: Bare Foot Practice 2

The suggestion is that phone and email work well together rather than as alternatives to each other. I have come to appreciate the strengths of working within the parameters of the letter and phone line, both for supervising networks and for working with practitoners who are isolated in practice.

Five point contracting for email and phone supervision.

I. Making a fitting space and time to focus on the work.

This includes ground rules, frequency, duration, availability, 'out of hours' and partnership or locum arrangements, cancellations and fees. Writing the 'hard' contract.

Who is professionally, legally and ethically responsible for the supervisees' practice when the client is not seen by the supervisor? A 'consultancy' contract for supervision conducted entirely by phone and email may be the most appropriate. This means the supervisee consults the supervisor but does not make them responsible for the practice. The supervisor is of course still ethically responsible to the supervisee for the supervision given. The supervisee may still make a professional agreement with the supervisor, the professional body and their school, to work within the parameters of the supervision.

Files sent by email are not secure. Check that full names and any identifying details of all parties are not sent. Full detail case notes can be sent by post after all.

What is paid for and how? Does the fee for a booked phone session include reasonable preparation or is this to be accounted for separately? What is reasonable preparation? What is to be kept on record and how? (Email correspondence generally forms a part of the supervision record.) How are telephone sessions recorded? Do you use a supervision record / a 'case top sheet' or both? What additional local support does the Supervisee have — for locum, 'acute' cover, peer support?

2. Getting clear about our intentions and expectations in being in the relationship.

What are realistic expectations for support and feedback in a relationship conducted entirely by phone and email? Since neither the client or supervisee meet with the supervisor and all case materials are read by the supervisor without the supervisee present.

The supervisee needs to be able to practice somewhat independently. This is not a useful form of supervision for those beginners in practice who require a lot of hands on support.

There is plenty of room for fantasy in a relationship conducted entirely by email and phone so that attention to case notes and asking questions to keep the relationship grounded in a working alliance may characterise this form of supervision more than one in which all participants are present in the room. Case notes need to make clear what is a verbatim report, what is observed, what the practitioner's interventions are and what is interpreted.

What is appropriate to do by email and what by phone? Email is great for sending case notes and summaries. Phone is generally better for giving sensitive and tentative feedback.

I am much more challenging, albeit tentatively, in my questioning on the phone than I am with the supervisee present. I need to know that the supervisee can support her action as I can't directly observe what is happening. I find that these supervisees become competent very quickly both in reflective writing and in cultivating their own supervisory voices. They have to. They tend to be less dependent upon the supervisor and are prepared to take difficult decisions sooner than some other student practitioners. They also tend to express a need at times for me to 'take the decision for them' from reading case notes alone. This is unsafe practice generally since I have no direct observation of the client in question. A phone call in which we remember what they do know and re-vision the way ahead together will usually resolve the feeling of helplessness and a need to have it done for them.

I like email/phone supervision since it gives me no choice but to supervise. I am not so tempted to move in on their practice and do it my way.

3. Being clear about commitment, boundaries and flexibility.

Commitment — The relationship is no less important for being conducted by phone and email. The phone appointment in the diary is as firm as any other client or supervisee appointment.

Boundaries and Flexibility — Is there sufficient time to prepare for the session between sending/ receiving case material by email and the telephone supervision? Emails can be sent at anytime. This can mean that expected turnaround times get shorter than we can manage. How often are we both going to check the mail box? Acknowledging receipt of emails and giving a time by which a reply can be expected is one way to keep the pressure down.

Some of the things people say about conducting phone consultations:

"I find that only having the voice to listen to focuses us on the task wonderfully and we get a lot of work done in the hour."

"I like that I can follow the sun around the house when taking the phone call rather than needing to stay in the study."

"I 'wake up' from a phone call, barely able to remember where I am. I have been away in the Rocky mountains or out in a desert practice with my supervisee."

4. Being clear about accountability including when things go wrong.

Who are we each accountable to for our work together?

Who needs to see records of the supervision?

Where can we each go to get independent supervision of issues arising in the relationship?

Guidance for three-cornered contracting comes in here.

5. Making time to reflect on the working relationship and re-contracting where necessary.

Making regular time in the phone session to review the work together and perhaps writing a reflective summary of the process in preparation for each session, encourages an open and learning attitude towards staying with the relationship through good and difficult times. See to guidelines for Working Alliance.

Mapping the Process 2

Any of the generic supervision models will work equally well for a phone and email relationship, group or self supervision. ('Vital Kit, Making and Maintaining Working Relationship,' Contracting – Mapping The Process1)

One way to map a telephone supervision is described in some detail here. I have chosen to focus on structure using Page and Wosket's Cyclical Model because a phone session may disintegrate into chat precisely because it can be conducted any place, any time anywhere!

Both draw a circle at the beginning of a session. Beginning at the top write in ' Contracting.' Moving clockwise round the circle write in 'Focus' 'Space' 'Bridge' and 'Review' and back again to meet with 'Contracting' (from Page and Wosket, 1994. Cyclical model).

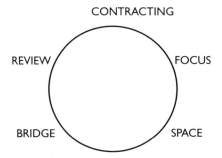

At either end of the telephone, we each have a circle representing in this scenario, the time limited session. Beginning with 'Contracting:' What are we here to do? What are the expectations?

Then what is the focus of this session? This is where we start to clarify the nature of the stuckness or issues brought.

The 'Space' is where we develop the work; where we can play, try things out, develop the story, work with different maps, models and perspectives. We can get lost in the space; making connections between one thought or image and another, between personal and professional development, between a case and a remedy or a client and an intervention.

The 'Bridge' is where we start to bring it on home, asking the question

"So how does this exploration impact on practice? How does it help me respond to this person or resolve this difficulty?"

We are now 50 minutes into a session and reviewing. What did I bring? What did I hope to get out of it? How has that changed and developed? Where have we been together? What next?

Re-contracting now for a different use of the time, for more or less time in the space, more or less focus, more or less preparation, or for more or less frequent sessions. Then for 'empty' sessions that aren't crowded out with an urgent need to respond or for more case focus or more spacious sessions to reflect, to play, to loosen up…

Working in different contexts can take us out of our comfort zones waking us up to what is happening rather than being left to sleep in our familiar and comfortable routines.

A Homeopathic and Supervisory Model for Assessment

We are engaged in making judgements all the time — from moment to moment interventions to assessing a student practitioner's competence to practice at the end of a course. A triad of self-assessment with feedback and according to shared criteria meets both these needs in a professional context.

This simple model describes a homeopathic and supervisory approach to assessment. It is a model for mature practice in that an attitude of independence with relatedness is required. It isn't developmental so much as adult to adult or 'I'm O.K., you're O.K.'

It is guided by the principles of a supervisory and homeopathic relating:

Observing without attachment or blame — especially important in the context of assessment.

Getting alongside each unique individual.

Minimum and energetic intervention.

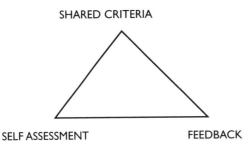

SHARED CRITERIA

SELF ASSESSMENT   FEEDBACK

Shared Criteria Moderate Standards

These are the expectations we share. For example, I am coming to you for help in recovering from asthma. I will be assessing the effectiveness of your approach in relation to that. It is asthma I expect to recover from. It is my asthma you have agreed to treat even when your model is to treat the individual person with asthma. As we work together, me expressing my asthma and you sharing your model of health and disease, this expectation may develop as connections are made and working relationship develops. For example, I remember an eczema I used to have and treated with cortisone cream after which the asthma began.

We may share some criteria and agree to differ on others. The point is to share some criteria by which we can both assess progress. These may well not be written down as a contract. Some aspects will be, for example, a professional code of ethics and practice outlining the criteria for ethical relationship in this context.

In a student situation shared criteria will be those elements that are understood by everyone in the school to define competence to practice. They will be written down and attached to syllabus and learning outcomes for different classes and assignments.

Shared criteria are those expectations we can both refer to in order to see how we are getting on. To be effective as criteria they need to be clear, owned by everyone involved, realistic and observable. Competent criteria will be both generic enough to adapt to different situations over time and specific enough to be observable in context by everyone involved.

Self Assessment Fosters Independence

"It's my asthma. I know how it feels, what it's like and what it stops me from doing. I have regular peak flow readings to help me assess improvement in lung capacity" (part of shared criteria).

"It's my learning. I know where I am and what interests me at the moment. I'm finding out what motivates me to carry on this course. I am finding out what I want to do in practice. I can see what I'm not paying attention to, in focussing where I am, by referring to the syllabus and assignments" (part of shared criteria).

To be homeopathic, assessment begins with each unique individual situation. The shared criteria remind us there is a bigger picture. Self-assessment shares the same pros and cons as self-supervising — a lack of feedback can leave us isolated, narcissistic, wilful and with a distorted image of ourselves and our competence. An overdependence on feedback leaves us lacking in confidence, creativity and competence.

Feedback Fosters Relatedness.

Homeopathic feedback gets alongside the other; is intended to help us go where we are heading and reminds us both of the shared criteria. This is true whether that feedback is in the form of a remedy, a tutor's response to a student or a supervisor's to another's clinical practice. (See Feedback in 'Vital Kit, Triading.')

The shared criteria themselves give me feedback — *'I feel better and the peak-flow readings tell me my lung capacity is improving too.' 'I'm focussing on learning to use the repertory and the syllabus timetable tells me I'm bang on schedule.'* Self assessment and feedback are alongside each other here.

Feedback that 'interrupts' the 'comfort' story is going to move us along: *"You use the word 'inspiration' a lot as in ' I can breathe in more easily' also 'my job doesn't inspire me anymore' and 'she doesn't inspire confidence' etc...."* the practitioner says to the patient with improving asthma.

"Your work is always completed in a timely manner. You are always on task. I have a strong image of the course from reviewing your work and not yet a sense of how this is for you; what the tension might be between your own pace and that demanded by the course..." the tutor says to a student.

And feedback to the author?

In writing this book I have tried to keep in view the criteria of showing homeopathic and supervisory relationship in different contexts. I hope this thread runs true. I have tried to be *supervisory* and *homeopathic* as much as talk about them: The tale of *Tuberculinum* (Chapter One) for example, pushes restlessly at the restrictions of a more conventional beginning to a supervision book. Cheetah (Chapter Three) and The Dog's Story (Chapter Seven) track the tale down through known and unknown territories. *Mercurius* (Chapter Four) is slippery and hard to stay focussed on. I hope these stories speak to you in this way of the essence of the matter. Your feedback in reading and using this book is most eagerly awaited. www.seachangeuk.com for contact details.

GLOSSARY IN CONTEXT

Active Listening: Listening with intent; paying attention to self, the other and the space between.

Aesthetic distance: To re-create an action in another form; to make a metaphor; something similar in essence and different in form. A homeopathically prescribed remedy is at an aesthetic distance from the dis-ease.

Allopathy: To do something different from the dis-ease; an anti-inflammatory or anti-biotic for example.

Art-play: The process of making an aesthetic distance; a proving, drama, sculpture, story making, poetry, metaphor, modelling, music making etc.

Burn Out: Disembodiment: The cycle of listening to self, other and the space, is broken. Recovery begins with listening to our bodies.

Case: The art-work we make of a person's dis-ease according to our healing modality. Part of making an aesthetic distance.

Cause: The myriad elements of a story that come together to manifest dis-ease, including miasm: Every dis-ease having countless causes and unknown effects. 'Susceptibility' expresses causation in dis-ease more accurately than 'cause.'

Coach: Guidance in performance of specific tasks.

Comfort story: Those we tell to make sense of our lives and that are known to us.

Critical incident: Anything that happens to give us pause, indicating there may be something here to re-member, learn from or celebrate.

Cure: Freedom to adapt and act with integrity in changing environments. At ease with oneself and the world.

Dis-ease: Energetic disturbance with its unique character as expressed in the phrase 'I am not myself.' It is subjectively felt and may or may not be objectively known as disease.

Disease: Particular signs, symptoms and tissue changes commonly associated with a named disease state that can be observed and recorded. Example: Fever, sweat and chills with influenza.

Dramatic Re-creation: Re-creating a situation, practice or dis-ease state at an aesthetic distance through drama; letting the characters develop their own voices and actions.

Dynamis: Motive force.

Dynamic Supervision: Attention to what is happening at the level of action and motivation.

Echo: The dis-owned dynamis is echoed in the supervision; the dis-ease state, which may not be perceived in the practice, is acted out in the supervision.

Elemental Story: The motive force, drive or dynamis behind the story. Perceived in action, movement, dream, metaphor, fears, cravings and aversions. The story that 'tells us.' The elemental story is connected to homeostasis.

Embodiment: Awareness of bodily means of expression including somatic symptoms of dis-ease and felt-sense. Embodiment as a means of re-creating practice — through physical, sensory experience — movement, dance, sculpture, warm ups etc.

Empathy: Fellow feeling.

E-Motion: Feeling connected to movement. Feelings come and go. E-motion is connected to the elemental story; to the tendency to homeostasis. It is non human specific, related to motive force.

Empty Relationship: One whose purpose is to inquire into another relationship. It exists only in so far as the inquiry continues. It is characterised by role and task: Supervision, Therapy.

Expert Practice: New situations, people and dis-ease states are understood and categorised in relation to what is already known.

Feedback: Consequences of thought and action. Response made with intent in supervisory and therapeutic relationship; the response of observers /observing aspect to a piece of practice.

Felt-sense: Feeling located in the body. A sensation that comes with a feeling tone — a lump in the throat that comes with a feeling of sadness for example.

Fusing: Becoming a part of the dis-ease story depending on individual susceptibility. See 'proving.'

Getting Alongside: Getting in step with another. Acknowledging the direction and pace.

Hering's Law: Described by Constanine Hering. (1800–1880) Cure, that is recovery of integrity, moves from the inside out, from more vital to less vital organs and systems and in the reverse order of appearance. This observation holds true whatever the healing modality.

Homeopathic aggravation: Healing crisis: Heightening of the experience of dis-ease through getting alongside it and therfore emphasising it's movement. This heightening may either go unnoticed or be observed moving according to Herings Law. If it is a healing aggravation it accompanies a sense of ease and well being.

Homeric Simile: A simile which goes on all the way through a story; a red thread; a motif repeated to form a pattern.

Inclusion: Awareness of myself, you and the relationship between us.

I-Thou: (Buber) Moment of oneness with another.

Interruption: 'Waking–up' to the dynamis; from the sleep of the 'comfort story' in actively listening to what is happening to self, other and the space in between.

Like cures like: Homeopathic principle of healing that a curative response is promoted by a vital stimulus similar in nature to the dis-ease.

Life Force: Dynamis. Vital force. That which animates us; moves us; that doesn't displace nor reside in any particular organ or system but 'governs with unbounded sway.' (Hahnemann, *Organon of Medicine*)

Mentor: Guide. Person who has gone before.

Meta comment: Observing "I." The story telling.

Metaphor: A figure of speech in which a name or phrase is given to an action or object not literally described by it but rather to express its elemental or essential nature.

Miasm: (Hahnemann, 1828) Theory of origins of dis-ease as individual susceptibility to named, genetically transmitted or acquired patterns of dis-ease. Miasm theory corresponds to belief that the roots of all suffering are in attachment.

Minimum Intervention: The least response required to restore integrity, autonomy, and relatedness.

Mirroring: Embodying what is perceived of the other; reflecting in action, gesture, posture and words what is felt-sensed to be present. Mirroring happens naturally as we 'get alongside' another.

Modelling: Practicing stillness, active listening and presence in order to focus attention on the dynamis and away from the more literal or superficial narrative; Modelling an interaction in clay or as human sculpture; art-play for the purposes of inquiry.

Parallel Process: Echo

Potency, potentisation and potentised remedy: Power and influence. A potentised remedy is one in which the energetic power of the remedy is increased while its mass and therefore its possible toxicological effects are reduced. In this way a minimum intervention for optimum benefit is achieved. A substance is potentised by serial dilution and succussion. Insoluble substances are ground or triturated.

Presence: Quality of being in the moment, begins with embodiment.

Proving: Inquiry into the properties of a medicinal substance taken by a group of people who record what happens under supervision.

Re-creation: Art-play and reflection on practice for the purpose of inquiry. Specifically, re-creating practice at an aesthetic distance. Recreation referring to the restorative function of supervision too.

Reflection: Reflecting back to another in gesture and word what has been perceived in order to help raise awareness of it.

Reflective Practice: On a continuum with 'expert' practice, reflective practice expects the unexpected. Expertise resides with the client and the interaction as much as with the practitioner's prior experience and knowledge 'Reflection in action' refers to moment to moment awareness, 'reflection on action' to considering an interaction afterwards. See 'Re-creation.'

Re-framing: Perceiving a situation in a different light as a result of supervision. The questions we bring to supervision aren't so much answered as re-framed so that we can move with them.

Simile: Something which is similar in form or function to something else.

Supervision: A quality of looking without attachment, fear or favour at 'what is.' Over view. The meta commentary, "observing I" or story telling. It is aspirational and 'good enough; a practice not a perfect. It begins with embodiment — being present to experience.

Susceptibility: 'Achilles heel,' individual weakness. Related to unique competence or adaptation: We each tend to our characteristic homeostasis, according to individual susceptibility. An admixture of inherited (miasmatic) and acquired response to dis-easing influences.

Symptoms: Expressions of our best attempts to adapt to internal or external stressors. Symptoms are objectively noted in disease or subjectively felt in dis-ease.

Triad: Practicing in threes; Presenter, receiver and observing aspect.

Unconditional Positive Regard: Acceptance; unconditional loving; acknowledging ; 'what is.'

Unprejudiced Observation: Accepting 'what is.'

Vital force: Life force.

REFERENCES

Andrews, B. 1998+ Conversations.

Assilem, M. 1994. "The Mad Hatters Tea Party" Society of Homeopaths seminar. London.

Assilem, M. 1997. *Lac Lupinum* presentation, Society of Homeopaths Annual Conference. Keele.

Astley, N. ed. 2002, *Staying Alive*. Bloodaxe; U.K.

Atkins, S. and K. Murphy. 1996. *Continuing Education in Nursing*, No. 329. U.K.

Balint, M. 1959. *Thrills and Regressions*. Hogarth Press; London.

Berne, E. 1964. *Games People Play*. Grove Press; NY.

Bettleheim, B. 1976. *The Uses Of Enchantment*. Thames & Hudson.

Bion, W. 1961. *Learning From Experience*. Tavistock; London.

Bion, W. 1973. *Experiences in Groups: Relation Reader 1*. AK Rice Institute Series.

Buber, M. 1996 edition. *I and Thou*. Tr. W. Kaufman. Touchstone; NY.

Byron, Katie & S. Mitchell. 2002 *Loving What Is*. Rider.

Cameron, J. 1994. *The Artists Way*. Pan;London, Basingstoke, Oxford.

Carroll, M. 2001. Description of the 'supervisory life,' p. 78. 'The Spirituality of Supervision' in *Integretative Approaches to Supervision*. JKP; London & Philadelphia.

Carroll, M. 2000. Iron Mill seminar, 'Supervision of Teams and Organisations.'

Carroll, M. 1996 *Counselling Supervision Theory, Skills and Practice*. Cassell; London & Philadelphia.

Carroll, M. and E. Holloway. 1999. *Counselling Supervision in Context*. Sage; London, Thousand Oaks, New Delhi.

Carter, A. Ed. 1990. *The Virago Book of Fairy Tales*. Virago Press; London.

Casement, P. 1985. *On Learning From the Patient*. Routledge; London.

Castro, M. 1989. 'A Homeopath's Perspective' in *The Homeopath*. Vol. 8. No.9. Spring. pp. 108–121.

Chesner, A. & H. Hahn, eds. 2002. *Creative Advances in Groupwork*. JKP; London.

Clarkson, P. 1995. *The Therapeutic Relationship*. Whurr Publications; London.

Cohen, L. 1992. song: *Anthem on The Future* album. Sony; Columbia.

Da Masio, A. 2003. *Looking For Spinoza*. Heinemann; London.

Dalal, F. 1988. *Taking The Group Seriously*. JKP; London.

Doehrman. 1976:4; in Hawkins & Shohet 2000 *Supervision in the Helping Professions*. OUP; Buckingham & Philadelphia.

Enslin. 1977; Seminar in Grossinger: *Planet Medicine*. 1980. p. 369–70. Shambhala; Boulder & London.

Gibbs. 1988; in Bulman, C. (Ed) in Chapter 3 'The Mentor's Experience - A Personal Perspective.' Brigid Reid in *Reflective Practice in Nursing*. Blackwell; London.

Gilbert, M and K. Evans. 2000. *Psychotherapy Supervision an integrative Relational approach*. OUP; Buckingham & Philadelphia.

Gleick, J. 1988. *Chaos: The Making of a New Science*. Heinemanns; London.

Graves, R. 1966. *The Greek Myths*. The Folio Society.

Grossinger, R. 1980. *Planet Medicine*. Shambhala; Boulder and London.

Hahnemann, S. 1828. *Chronic Diseases, Their Nature and Homeopathic Treatment*. Arnold; Dresden.

Hahnemann, S. 1842. *Organon of Medicine,* 6th edition. Homeopathic Publications; New Delhi.

Hawkins, P. 2002. Bath Centre for Staff Team Development Seminar on Supervisison of Teams and Organisations.

Hawkins, P. and R. Shohet. 2000. *Supervision in the Helping Professions*. 2nd ed. OUP; Buckingham & Philadelphia.

Hewson, J. 1999. Notes from Diploma in Supervision and Mentoring. The Iron Mill Institute (unpublished).

Hillman, J. 1965. *Suicide and the Soul*. Spring Publications; Connecticut.

Holloway, E.L. 1995. *Clinical Supervision: A Systems Approach*. Sage; Thousand Oaks, CA.

Holloway, E. and M. Carroll (eds.). 1999. *Training Counselling Supervisors*. Sage; London,Thousand Oaks New Dehli.

Houston, G. 1984. *The Red Book of Groups*. Rochester Foundation; London.

Houston, G. 1990. *Supervision and Counselling*. Rochester Foundation; London.

Inskipp, F and B. Proctor. 1995. *The Art , Craft and Tasks of Counselling Supervision.* Cascade; Twickenham.

Jenkyns, M. 1997. 'Gender Issues in Supervision' in *Dramatherapy Theory and Practice 3.* Sue Jennings, Ed. Routledge; London & NewYork.

Jennings, S. 1994. 'The Theatre of Healing: Metaphor and Metaphysics in the Healing Process' in S. Jennings, A. Cattanach, S Mitchell, A Chesner and B. Meldrum (eds) *The Handbook of Dramatherapy.* Routledge; London.

Jennings, S. 1998. 'Ariadne's Ball of Thread' in *Introduction to Dramatherapy Theatre and Healing.* JKP; London & NewYork..

Jung, C.G. 1979. *Man and His Symbols.* Aldus; London.

Kagan, N. 1980. Influencing human interaction — Eighteen years with IPR, in A.K. Hess (ed) *Psychotherapy Supervision,* Wiley; NY.

Kaplin, B. 2001. *The Homeopathic Conversation, The art of taking the case.* Natural Medicine Press; London.

Kaptchuck, T. & M. Croucher. 1986. *The Healing Arts.* BBC; London.

Kennelly, B. in Astley, N. 2002. *Staying Alive.* p. 93. Bloodaxe; U.K.

Landy, R.J. 1986. *Dramatherapy. Concepts and Practices.* Charles Thomas; Springfield, Ill.

Logue, C. in Astley. 2002. *Staying Alive.* Bloodaxe; U.K.

Maturana, H.R. & F. Varela. 1984. *The Tree of Cognition* in Tselikas-Portman. 1999. *Supervision and Dramatherapy.* JKP; London & Philadelphia.

Metzger, Deena. 1992. *Writing For Your Life.* Harper; San Fransisco.

Morissette, P.J. *Self-Supervision.* Brunner, Routledge; NY.

Murray Preece, A. 2004 in conversation. www.mudra.co.uk.

Nicholls, P. 2001. *A Voyage for Madmen.* Harper Collins; NewYork.

Nitsun, M. 1996. *The Anti-Group: Destructive Forces in the Group and Their Creative Potential.* Routledge; London.

Norland, M. *Mappa Mundi and the Dynamics of Change.* Adam Martanda.

Norland. M. 1998. 'A few thoughts about receiving the case.' *The Homeopath.* No. 69. Spring. p.10.

Norland, M. 2003. *Signatures Miasms Aids.* Yondercott Press; Abergavenny.

Oliver, M. In Astley, N. ed. 2002. *Staying Alive.* p. 78. Bloodaxe; U.K.

Page, S. and V. Wosket, 1994. *Supervising the Counsellor.* Routledge; London & New York.

Parry, A. & R. Doan. 1994. *Story Revisions.* The Guilford Press; New York.

Pinkhola, Estes C. 1992. *Women Who Run With The Wolves.* Rider; London, Sydney, Aukland, Johannesburg.

Pirani, A. 1988. *The Absent Father: Crisis and Creativity.* Routledge; New York.

www.poetrymagic.co.uk. 2003 & 2004. A poetry discussion site.

Proctor, B. 2000. *Group Supervision.* Sage; London, Thousand Oaks, New Dehli.

Ram Dass & P. Gorman. 1986. *How Can I help?* 1986 Rider; London, Sydney, Aukland, Johannesburg.

Rogers, C. 1961. *A therapists view of Psychotherapy. On Becoming a Person.* Constable; London.

Ryan, S. 2002. 'What's in a Case?' in *The Homeopath.* No. 85. Spring. pp. 13–17.

Sankaran, R. 1994. *The Substance of Homeopathy.* Homeopahic Medical Publishers, Bombay.

Sankaran, R. 2002. *An Insight into Plants.* Vol. 1. Homeopathic Medical Publishers; Mumbai.

Sankaran, R. 2003. Cheetah notes from seminar Goa, India

Scholten, J. 1996. *Homeopathy and the Elements.* Stichting; Alonissos.

Schon, D. A. 1983. *The Reflective Practitioner.* Temple Smith; London.

Schon, D. A. 1987. *Educating the Reflective Practitioner.* Jossey Bass.

Sherr, J. 1991. *The Homœopathic Proving of Hydrogen.* Dynamis Books; Malvern.

Sherr, J. 1994 *The Dynamics and Methodology of Homeopathic Provings.* Dynamis Books; Malvern.

Sherr, J. 2002. *Dynamic Materia Medica: Syphilis.* Dynamis Books; Malvern.

Shipton, G. Ed. 1997. *Supervision of Psychotherapy and Counselling - making a place to think.* OUP; Buckingham&Philadelphia.

Shohet, R. 1985. *Dream Sharing.* Crucible; Thorsons, Northamptonshire.

Shohet, R. 2002 in conversation.

Stern, D. 2004. *The Present Moment in Psychotherapy and Everyday Life.* Norton.

Thompson, S. 1999. *The Group Context.* JKP; London & Philadelphia.

Townsend, I. 2004. 'Almost Nothing To Do — Supervision and the Person-Centred Approach in Homeopathy' in Tudor, E. and M. Worral, Eds. *Freedom to Practice Person-centred approaches to supervision.* CCS Books; Ross-On-Wye.

Townsend, I. 2001. 'Manning The Lifeboats; Or sailing the seas with confidence? Supervision in the service of a profession' in *NASH News.* Spring edition. USA

Tselikas-Portman, E. 1999. *Supervision and Dramatherapy.* p. 27. JKP; London & Philadelphia.

Tyler, M. 1952. 2nd ed. *Homeopathic Drug Pictures.* C .W. Daniel; Saffron Walden.

Vermeulen, F. 1996. *Synoptic Materia Medica II.* Merlin Publishers; Haarlem.

Walker, A. *Horses Make a Landscape Look More Beautiful.* 1985. The Womens Press; London.

Whitman, W. 1855/1973 Edition *Leaves Of Grass.* From 'Song of Myself.' W.W. Norton & Co. Inc.; New York.

Whitmont, E. 1983. *The Return of the Goddess.* JKP; London & Philadelphia.

Wosket, Val. 1999. *The Therapeutic Use of Self.* Routledge; London & New York.

INDEX

About the Author

Sheila Ryan is a fellow of The Society of Homeopaths and Clinical Principal at the School of Homeopathy, Devon. She practices in Dorset where she lives with her husband and son.

'Vital Practice' workshops for group facilitators, supervisors and supervisees are run regularly on the Isle of Portland in Dorset, England. Contact: see www.seachangeuk.com.